Collectors' Coins: Great Britain
2018
By C H Perkins

C000180698

British gold, silver and base metal coins. Their
values, specifications and varieties, 1760 - 1970.

2018, 43rd Edition © 2017

ISBN: (printed edition)
978 0 948964 91 6
This title is also available as an eBook.

A wealth of numismatic information and a compilation of averaged selling-prices
drawn from dealers' lists, coin auctions, numismatic magazines and experience in
the trade.

Errors and Omissions:
Every effort has been made to ensure that the information and price data contained within this book
is accurate and complete. However, errors do sometimes have a habit of creeping in unnoticed, and with this in
mind the following email address has been established for notifications of omissions and errors:
info@rotographic.com. Readers within the UK can also call the telephone number below.

Thanks to everyone involved.

www.rotographic.com
020 308 69996

In Association with Predecimal
predecimal.com

* This book is not endorsed or supported by the British Numismatic Trade Association, it has simply been
written by one of its members. See www.bnta.net for further details on the BNTA.

Printed by: www.standart.lt

CONTENTS

INTRODUCTION

Welcome to "COLLECTORS' COINS GREAT BRITAIN 2018". CCGB is the comprehensive British coin price-guide covering British coins from the reign of King George III to 1970.

There has been a longer gap than usual between the last edition and this new, 43rd edition. Basically - and it pains me to say - this is due to lower demand for a pre-decimal UK coinage guide! The UK went decimal 47 years ago and the last remaining 'old money' disappeared from circulation in the early 1990s (the shillings and florins were in use as 5p and 10p up to when the coins were made smaller in size). My 'Collectors' Coins - UK Decimal Issues' book is doing a roaring trade since I removed the decimal coins from this book and created a much more comprehensive book just for the newer coins - the decimal book covers 1968 onwards and is already thicker than this one, which covers over 200 years of coinage.

No one under about 52 has experienced paying for things in £SD and very few people under about 30 have ever been exposed to a pre-decimal coin out in the wild. The youngest two generations have no nostalgic connection to the money in this book and I think that is one of the main factors leading to the decline in the popularity of collecting 'old money'. It remains popular of course, and there will always be collectors, but it can be hard to win over new ones. Younger people still collect coins, some of them very passionately, but they tend to stick with what they know and are kept so busy (for better or worse) with the plethora of new annual coin issues. Many never have a chance to explore what went before.

There probably are other factors that result in lower interest in books on pre-decimal coins; the internet is no doubt one of them and the first place many people turn to when they want to establish the value of an old coin - which for the odd coin can probably be reliable, but for others it can open a very large can of worms and result in more questions than answers!

In this book I have given all the prices a thorough going-over and have also added mintage numbers for the gold sovereign based denominations.

Good luck with your collection or your price research.
C H Perkins, November 2017

OUR TITLES

Established in 1959, Rotographic have been publishing reference books in the UK since the mid 1960s. The original "Check Your Change" series published until 1971 sold over 1.75 million copies, making it probably the biggest selling coin book ever! There are currently 12 titles in print, some of which are shown here. All of the titles are available in printed form and most also as eBooks (e.g. for Amazon Kindle).

Previous Cover!

CC - DECIMAL ISSUES OF THE UK
ISBN 978 0 948964 92 3 (NEW ED. IN EARLY 2018)

RRP
£7.35

- A COMPREHENSIVE GUIDE TO ALL DECIMAL COINAGE UP TO 2018 PLUS CURRENT ENGLISH BANKNOTES
- ONE OF THE UK'S BEST SELLING COIN BOOKS
- AUTHORITATIVE CURRENT INFORMATION
- ERROR COINS AND VARIETIES
- ALL DECIMAL CIRCULATION TYPES ILLUSTRATED AND VALUED

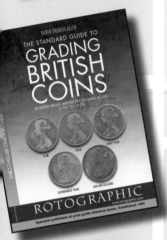

GRADING BRITISH COINS
(THE STANDARD GUIDE TO). ISBN 978 0 948964 56 5

RRP
£9.95

- AN IMPORTANT UNIQUE NUMISMATIC PUBLICATION
- LEVELS OF WEAR ILLUSTRATED AND DESCRIBED
- NEW PAPERBACK B/W EDITION
- GREAT FOR NOVICES AND EXPERIENCED COLLECTORS.
- ALL UK PRE-DECIMAL COINS 1797 - 1970 COVERED

ENGLAND'S STRIKING HISTORY
ISBN 978 0 948964 85 5

RRP
£7.95

- GENERAL HISTORICAL INFORMATION ABOUT ENGLAND FROM 959AD TO 1662.
- LEARN TO DIFFERENTIATE BETWEEN THE HUGE VARIETY OF HAMMERED SILVER COINS, WITH LOTS OF ILLUSTRATIONS.
- 148 PAGES.

ROMAN COINS (2 TITLES)
ISBN 978 0 948964 54 1 (SILVER), 978 0 948964 48 0 (BASE)

£6.30 RRP EACH

- ROMAN BASE METAL COINS - A PRICE GUIDE.
- ROMAN SILVER COINS - A PRICE GUIDE.
- CHRONOLOGICAL INFORMATION ABOUT THE COINAGE OF THE ROMANS.
- HUNDREDS OF ACCURATE ILLUSTRATIONS AND VALUATIONS.

BRITISH MILITARY MONEY
ISBN 978 0 948964 49 7

RRP
£5.95

- BRITISH MILITARY AUTHORITY NOTES.
- TRIPOLITANIA.
- BRITISH ARMED FORCES, ALL SERIES.
- VALUES, SIZES AND OTHER INFORMATION.

CAMPAIGN MEDALS (2 TITLES)
VOL. 1 - 19TH CENTURY. VOL. 2 - 20TH CENTURY.

FROM
£6.95

- HISTORICAL CAMPAIGN BACKGROUND INFORMATION.
- FULLY ILLUSTRATED IN COLOUR.
- MARKET VALUES FOR UK AND IRISH/EMPIRE MEDALS.
- VOL. 1: ISBN 978 0948964 64 0. VOL. 2: ISBN 978 0 948964 44 2

NEW! THE COIN COLOURING BOOK
ISBN 978 0 948964 89 3

RRP
£6.99

- 36 COIN LINE DRAWINGS TO COLOUR-IN.
- FROM SIMPLE TO HIGHLY INTRICATE.
- CELTIC, HAMMERED AND MODERN COINS.
- INCLUDING HISTORICAL INFORMATION.

Two coloured-in pictures.

THE LAYOUT
Collectors' Coins Great Britain is laid out in three sections:

The **Main** section covers the period 1760-1970 and contains the main "Collectors' Coins", that is; all non-proof coins that were issued for circulation and the common mass produced proof coins. This section also covers some of the extremely rare coins of Edward VIII.

The **Gold** section covers Guineas, and fractions thereof struck 1760 to 1813 and Half Sovereigns, Sovereigns, Two Pound Coins and Five Pound coins struck from 1817 to 1968

The **Maundy** section contains Maundy sets and singles. These were never meant for circulation and are not proofs, so they too have been moved away from the general circulation section. As a bonus the proof sets from 1826 onwards are listed before the Maundy section.

HOW TO USE THIS PRICE GUIDE
The first (Main) and second (Gold) sections of this book are arranged in ascending order of face value, starting with the Fractional Farthing and working right up to the gold five pound coin. Each denomination is introduced and average size and weight data is also given. Each denomination is arranged in ascending date order, with each change in monarch clearly stated as well as major changes in the coin type.

All listings are split into columns, with a column each for the Date, Reference number (see next page), Mintage figure (also see next page) and the market values in 2-4 different grades. The Gothic florins have an extra column to show the date in Roman numerals and some of the Crowns have an extra column for the regnal edge year.

MINTAGE FIGURES

It is very important to note that the mintage figures quoted in this book are very rarely accurate. Until the 1950's the Royal mint did not record the number of coins with a given date, but rather the number of coins struck in a particular year. So for example, the mintage of 1836 Farthings may be quoted as 1,290,240, but it is perfectly possible that a large proportion of those could have been dated 1835 (or even 1837). The mintage numbers do not record the number of coins that for certain types were re-melted either, so don't place any real relevance on the mintage numbers. They are just there to give a general feel for the numbers of coins produced.

INFORMATION ABOUT THE REFERENCE NUMBERS

Throughout the main section, usually in the second column, you will notice there are reference numbers. The column in which these numbers appear will either be labeled 'PECK', 'FMAN' or 'ESC' and these abbreviations represent the books from which the reference number is taken. Many dealers will quote the numbers in these books when selling coins, as well as the date and condition. Every pre-decimal non gold coin in this catalogue has been labeled with its reference number from the following publications:

PECK = English Copper, Tin and Bronze Coins in the British Museum 1558-1958, by C Wilson Peck. All the Peck numbers in this book are preceded with a 'P' and all the Copper and Brass coins in this book are cross referenced with the Peck volume. Peck Numbers are sometimes referred to by other publications as 'BMC' (British Museum Collection).

FMAN = The Bronze Coinage of Great Britain, by Michael J Freeman (also published by Rotographic). This book, which is generally thought of as more up to date with Bronze coinage has been used to provide the reference numbers for all the Bronze coins in this book. Bronze coins were made from 1860 onwards.

ESC = English Silver Coinage since 1649, by P Alan Rayner. This book has been used to provide reference numbers for all the Silver and Cupro-Nickel coins. Note that a new edition of this book was published in September 2015, updated by Maurice Bull and with different coin numbering. The numbers in this book are from the 1992 edition - I feel that particular edition is currently the most widely used.

It is also important to bear in mind that not all of the coins listed in this book are referred to in the listed reference volumes, and where this is the case the initials **ND** (Not Distinguished) will appear in the reference number column. The initials **MV** are also used in places to indicate that Minor Varieties exist.

AN INTRODUCTION TO BRITISH COIN GRADING

The columns containing the market values in this book are headed by 2-4 Standard British coin grade names. Even novice coin collectors will probably realise that coins that are in better than average condition are always worth more than coins that have seen lots of circulation. For an excellent pictorial guide to grading British coins, there is a Rotographic publication entitled "The Standard Guide to Grading British Coins 1797-1970". Grading coins accurately takes a lot of experience in looking at the same types of coins, but, just as a rough idea this is what the grade abbreviations mean:

Poor: These are not just smooth disks but actually identifiable coins. However, the list of shortcomings can be extensive, ranging from a few letters obliterated in the legend, to coins in which virtually the only detail visible is the date. Very few coins will have a value over and above that of the metal content, and they would need to be pretty rare and sought after.

Fair/Good: Heavily worn, but with readable legend and major points of design identifiable. It would be reasonable to say that the vast bulk of 20th century coins in this condition are worth no more than their metal or face value. Generally speaking, it has never been practical to produce price data for coins in Fair condition, simply because coins are rarely collected as such.

F = Fine: Fine coins show considerable wear to all raised surfaces. Some detail should be visible on the designs and some of the main hair volume should be visible on the Monarch's head. Not individual strands, but maybe a parting or signs of head-dress. Many of the coins you receive now in your change, even after just 30 years or less of normal use would probably be Fine or less.

VF = Very Fine: A coin with some wear to the highest areas of the design but which has seen limited circulation. More hair detail is evident and also detail on the other designs. Just as an average guide a coin that has been in normal circulation for approximately 5 years may qualify for VF status.

EF = Extremely Fine: A coin with little sign of being circulated. There may be only the slightest wear to the highest areas and minimal scratches and other marks. Often some of the mint lustre is visible on coins of this grade. As a rough idea a coin in your change would probably be an EF if it had been fortunate and was minted just 1 year ago.

(Continued on the next page)

UNC = Uncirculated: Like the name suggests, the coin should be as it left the mint with no signs of circulation or wear. Not necessarily perfect though, because coins can pick up scratches and what are known as 'bag marks' during mass production and contact with other coins at the mint. The coin should have most of its lustre present and some dealers may expect 100% lustre on coins stated as Uncirculated. An Uncirculated coin would be given to you in your change from a freshly opened bag of new coins. So, as you can imagine, Uncirculated coins that are 30, 60 or even 200 years old, are often pretty rare, and very collectable, hence the higher prices for coins in this grade.

BU = Brilliant Uncirculated: BU is not really an official grade but is increasingly used to refer to an Uncirculated coin with full mint lustre. Such coins are also allowed to exhibit minor signs of mass production.

You may also see the grade FDC which is generally only used when talking about special proof strikings, and it means absolutely perfect in every way.

As well as the basic grades listed here, collectors will often encounter grades like 'GVF' for example. This indicates the coin is not exactly a 'VF' (Very Fine). In fact the 'G' stands for 'Good' so a GVF coin would be better that VF but not quite EF. 'N' stands for 'Near' and 'A' for 'About'. So, the range between VF and EF for example looks like this: VF, GVF, NEF, AEF, EF.

"The Standard Guide to Grading British Coins", also published by Rotographic and mentioned previously, is available from all reputable book-sellers. See www.rotographic.com or call **020 308 69996** for further details.

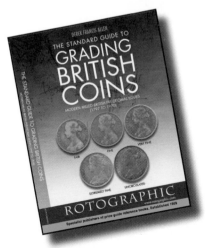

WHERE NO VALUE IS STATED

You will notice that for certain coin types only the higher grade columns are present. This is because these coins are not normally collected in lower grades. But that doesn't mean they are worthless in lower grades. Coins of all grades are there to be collected, and if you want to collect a date run of coins, then the grade doesn't really matter. There are some coins that have missing price data in one or more columns, this usually indicates that no data was available for that coin, in that grade.

SILVER BULLION VALUE

All British silver-coloured coins dated before 1947 contain silver, so even very worn coins are at least worth something. Silver coins dated pre 1920 are .925 (92.5% silver) and coins dated 1920-46 are .500 (50%) silver. The value of silver fluctuates, but generally dealers will gladly pay many times face value for all pre 1947 Silver coins. Decimal equivalent face values are as follows:

Each silver Threepence has a face value of 1/80th of a £ Sterling (1.25p).
Each Sixpence is 1/40th of a £ Sterling (2.5p).
Each Shilling is 1/20th of a £ Sterling (5p).
Each Florin is 1/10th of a £ Sterling (10p).
Halfcrowns are 1/8th of a £ Sterling (12.5p).
Crowns are a quarter of a £ Sterling, so 25p face value.

GOLD BULLION VALUE

Guineas and sovereign based coins that are very worn, coins that have been used as jewellery (with mounts welded to them or damaged edges for example) or modern common sovereigns are often just worth their bullion value. All the gold coins listed in this book are made of 22 carat gold which is 91.66% fine. The weights of the gold coins are given in their appropriate section.

MARKETING

It is generally accepted that a dealer's buying price for an individual coin or collection of individual coins is about 50-75% of his/her selling price. The precise deal will of course depend on how sought after the items are, and whether the dealer already has a buyer in mind. The dealer is in effect out of pocket until a buyer can be found. The dealer has to make a living, and will only make profit in the long term when the coins can be re-sold.

CLEANING/POLISHING AND HANDLING OF COINS

DO NOT go anywhere near any coins with any chemicals/abrasives, or anything harder than a soft toothbrush. If your coins are dirty and are low grade, by all means use soap and water and perhaps a toothbrush to remove loose dirt. Make sure they are thoroughly dried, especially copper based coins. High grade and proof coins should ideally be handled by the edges or with gloves, because even the slightest finger print may knock significant value from the coin. If you have a valuable coin with a cosmetic problem, consult an expert first, or simply try to live with it.

VARIETIES / IF IN DOUBT

This book contains the most comprehensive listing of British coin varieties available for all denominations. However, it doesn't list every single variety. Many minute differences would need a whole page to explain, and don't always affect the value of the coin. For this reason some have been left out. If you have any queries about varieties or the contents of this book please consult www.rotographic.com and any important points that are raised will be covered in the next edition.

For further information on coin collecting or buying coins and collecting accessories why not ask at the place you purchased this book. Or if this book was purchased from a book retailer, try an internet search on 'British Coins', 'British coins for sale' and similar phrases. A few adverts for reputable dealers are shown within this book.

All fractional farthings were originally issued for colonial use. However, half farthings were made legal tender in the United Kingdom from 1842 - 1869. For that reason all fractional farthings have been listed.

Quarter Farthings

The tiny copper quarter farthing was struck solely for use in Ceylon (Sri Lanka). The maundy twopence die was used for the obverse. William Wyon was responsible for creating both the obverse and reverse dies.

VICTORIA Young head. Copper 13.5mm. Weight 1.17g

Date	Peck	Mintage	Fine	VF	EF	UNC/BU
1839	P1608	3,840,000	£10	£22	£70	£100/£200
1851	P1609	Inc below	£20	£30	£70	
1852	P1610	2,215,000	£10	£25	£60	£100/£200
1853	P1612	Inc above	£15	£30	£75	£150/£200

Victoria 1839 Quarter Farthing

Third Farthings

Third Farthings were made for use in Malta. The farthing was already circulating at a face value of three Maltese grains so the third farthing was made to be exactly a third of the weight of a farthing, thus providing the Maltese with a coin of one grain face value. Obverse and reverse dies were by William Wyon.

GEORGE IV Copper 16mm. Weight 1.57g

Date	Peck	Mintage	Fine	VF	EF	UNC/BU
1827	P1453		£4	£10	£50	£150/

WILLIAM IV Copper 16mm. Weight 1.57g

Date	Peck	Mintage	Fine	VF	EF	UNC/BU
1835	P1477		£8	£20	£90	£200/

VICTORIA Young head. Copper 16mm. Weight 1.56g

Date	Peck	Mintage	Fine	VF	EF	UNC/BU
1844	P1606	1,301,040 Varieties exist	£20	£40	£100	£200/
1844	P1607	RE instead of REG.	£40	£80	£350	
1844		ND. RE instead of REG but thinner flan, 0.88g. AUNC: £650 Cooke 2006				

George IV and William IV Third Farthings.
The reverse types were the same.

Victoria 1844 Young
head Third Farthing

Third Farthings (continued)

Third farthings from this point onwards were struck in bronze (95% copper, 4% tin and 1% zinc). Not being strictly British, they are not listed in the Freeman reference book, so Peck numbers are quoted instead. Victoria's bust and the reverses are the work of Leonard Charles Wyon, based on a model by W Theed. The portrait of Edward VII was modelled by G W de Saulles, and the portrait of George V by Sir Bertram Mackennal.

VICTORIA Bun head. Bronze 15.5mm. Weight 0.95g

Date	Peck	Mintage	Fine	VF	EF	UNC/BU
1866	P1926	576,000	£4	£10	£25	£80/
1866	ND	No stop after D.G				£150/
1868	P1928	144,000	£5	£10	£25	£80/
1876	P1932	162,000	£4	£15	£30	£80/
1878	P1933	288,000 Large date	£3	£10	£20	£60/
1878	ND	Small date	Scarcer			
1881	P1934	144,000	£3	£8	£25	£100/
1884	P1936	144,000	£3	£5	£25	£60/
1885	P1937	288,000	£3	£6	£25	£60/

EDWARD VII Bronze 15.5mm. Weight 0.96g

Date	Peck	Mintage	Fine	VF	EF	UNC/BU
1902	P2241	288,000	£3	£5	£15	£30/£50

GEORGE V Bronze 15.5mm. Weight 0.93g

Date	Peck	Mintage	Fine	VF	EF	UNC/BU
1913	P2358	288,000	£2	£5	£15	£30/£50

George V 1913 Third Farthing

Half Farthings

The half farthing, like the quarter farthing was originally struck for use in Ceylon (Sri Lanka). Willam Wyon was responsible for the obverse and reverse dies of the three monarchs under which half farthings were struck. The half farthing was made legal tender in the United Kingdom in 1842 and remained so until the demonetization of all the (pre 1860) copper coinage in 1869.

GEORGE IV Laureate head. Copper 18mm. Weight 2.35g

Date	Peck	Mintage	Fine	VF	EF	UNC/BU
1828	P1446	7,680,000 Rev A	£10	£35	£100	£250/
1828	P1449	Rev B see below	£12	£30	£100	£200/
1828	ND	As above with large date. AVF: £200				
1830	P1450	8,776,320	£10	£30	£90	£280/
1830	ND	Smaller date	£50	£150	£250	
1830	P1451	Rev B see below	£40	£100	£200	

Rev A: The trident reaches above base of letters.
Rev B: The trident reaches base of letters.

William IV Copper 18mm. Weight 2.31g

Date	Peck	Mintage	Fine	VF	EF	UNC/BU
1837	P1476	1,935,360	£40	£100	£300	£500/

Victoria Young head, Copper 18mm. Weight 2.37g

Date	Peck	Mintage	Fine	VF	EF	UNC/BU
1839	P1590	2,042,880	£5	£8	£40	£100/
1842	P1592		£4	£8	£30	£100/
1843	P1593	3,440,640	£3	£8	£25	£80/
1844	P1594	6,451,000	£3	£8	£25	£80/
1844	P1595	E of REGINA over N	£10	£25	£80	£150/£300
1847	P1596	3,010,560	£4	£7	£30	£70/
1847	ND	Last R of BRITANNIA over an A				£200/
1851	P1597		£4	£10	£30	£90/
1851	ND	1st 1 over 5	£10	£40	£100	£200/£300
1851	ND	5 struck over blundered number			£100	£200/
1852	P1598	989,184	£6	£15	£40	£70/
1853	P1599	955,224	£10	£20	£60	£90/
1854	P1602	677,376	£10	£25	£90	£200/
1856	P1603	913,920	£20	£50	£100	£200/
1856	ND	Large Rev date and letters		£100	£250	

George IV Half Farthing obverse. The reverse type was almost identical to the William IV reverse, right.

George IV 1837 Half Farthing

Victoria 1844 Half Farthing

Farthings

The first official farthings bearing the portrait of George III were struck at the Tower (Royal) Mint in London. They were made without a collar, so are not perfectly round. Their size varies from about 23mm to 24.5mm and the weights also vary from around 4.3g to 5.3g. No mintage figures were recorded but it is known that the combined farthings and halfpennies struck between 1770 and 1775 totalled £46,455 in face value, which would have been enough to provide low millions of each denomination for each year (remember there were 480 halfpennies or 960 farthings to the pound)! An awful lot of the 1770s coppers were melted down and made into lightweight forgeries. Previous to this issue, in 1762-3 about 3.6 million farthings were minted using 1754 dated dies - these provided the public with much needed small change, but are numismatically indistinguishable from the actual 1754 farthings struck in that year, under George II.

GEORGE III Copper, about 24mm. Weight 4.93g (average)					
Date	Peck	Notes	Fine	VF	EF
1771	P909	Reverse varieties exist	£40	£80	£250
1771	ND	1st 7 over 1		£200	
1773	P911		£10	£50	£180
1773	P912	Obv. 1 No stop reverse	£40	£100	£220
1773	P913	Obverse 2	£25	£100	
1773	P914	Obv. 2 No stop reverse	£10	£40	£180
1773	ND	No stop after REX	£20	£50	
1774	P915	Obverse 1	£10	£35	£180
1774	P916	Obverse 2	£10	£30	£150
1775	P917		£10	£40	£150
1775	ND	Inverted A for V in GEORGIVS	£100	£300	

George III 1771 Farthing

The farthings of 1799, 1806 and 1807 were all struck by Matthew Boulton at his mint in Soho, Birmingham. For the first time ever, a denomination was marked on a British coin, as the 1799 farthing had "1 FARTHING" written in the exergue on the reverse. The Boulton Farthing dies were all engraved by Conrad Heinrich Küchler. The bust of George IV was by Pistrucci and the reverse was by William Wyon.

GEORGE III Copper 23.5mm. Weight 6.3g						
Date	Peck	Notes	Fine	VF	EF	UNC/BU
1799	P1279	3 Berries in wreath	£4	£10	£45	£100/
1799	P1280	4 Berries in wreath	£10	£20	£70	£120/

GEORGE III Copper 21mm. Weight 4.7g						
Date	Peck	Notes	Fine	VF	EF	UNC/BU
1806	P1396	Bust 1	£4	£10	£70	£150/
1806	P1397	Bust 2	£4	£10	£50	£140/
1806	P1398	Incuse dot on truncation	£15	£50	£100	£300/
1807	P1399	Bust 1	£4	£10	£50	£100/£200

Bust 1: Curls of side whiskers are incuse, and the lower wreath leaves each have overlapping strands of hair. **Bust 2:** Curls are not incuse and the wreath leaves have no overlapping hair.

George III 1799 Farthing

George III 1806 Farthing

GEORGE IV Laureate Head. Copper 22mm. Weight 4.75g

Date	Peck	Mintage	Fine	VF	EF	UNC/BU
1821	P1407	2,688,000	£2	£10	£40	£100/
1821	ND	G over O in GRATIA	£30		£200	(2009)
1822	P1409	5,924,352 Obv 1	£2	£10	£40	£100/
1822	P1411	Obv 2	£3	£10	£40	£100/
1823	P1412	2,365,440	£3	£12	£50	£100/
1823	P1413	Date has I for 1	£15	£40	£140	£300/
1825	P1414	4,300,800 Obv 1	£2	£15	£50	£120/
1825	ND	5 over higher 5	£30		£200	
1825	ND	D of DEI over U	£30	£80	£250	
1825	P1415A	Obverse 2	£4	£15	£50	£100/
1826	P1416	6,666,240	£10	£15	£50	£100/
1826	ND	GRATIA R over E	£15	£70	£250	

GEORGE IV Bare Head. Copper 22mm. Weight 4.75g

Date	Peck	Mintage	Fine	VF	EF	UNC/BU
1826	P1439	Mintage included above	£2	£10	£60	£100/
1826	ND	Roman I for 1		£80	£300	
1827	P1442	2,365,440	£3	£10	£50	£100/
1828	P1443	2,365,440	£3	£12	£60	£80/£100
1829	P1444	1,505,280	£5	£14	£60	£150/
1830	P1445	2,365,440	£5	£15	£50	£120/

George IV 1822 Farthing

George IV 1827 Farthing

1822 and 1825 Obverse varieties.

Obverse 1: The leaf-midribs are single raised lines (left image).

Obverse 2: The 3 lowest leaves have incuse midribs (right image).

When the coin dies became worn, weak letters and digits were re-cut using a punch. If the new letter or number was not exactly in the right place this led to the appearance of doubled and sometimes even trebled characters on the coin. This is commonplace during this period, however a major misalignment can add value to the coin.

William IV Copper 22mm. Weight 4.7g

Date	Peck	Mintage	Fine	VF	EF	UNC/BU
1831	P1466	2,68.8,000	£5	£20	£50	£120/
1834	P1470	1,935,360 Rev A	£50	£170	£400	
1834	P1471	Reverse B	£10	£30	£70	£120/
1835	P1472	1,720,320 Rev A	£5	£25	£70	£120/
1835	P1473	Reverse B	£4	£20	£80	
1836	P1474	1,290,240	£4	£20	£70	£120/
1837	P1475	3,010,560	£4	£25	£70	£120/
1837	ND	7 over 7 (misaligned)		£50	£200	

Reverse A has an incuse line down the arms of the saltire (St Andrews cross).
Reverse B has a raised line down the arms of saltire.

William IV 1837 Farthing.

VICTORIA Young head. Copper 22mm. Weight 4.7g

Date	Peck	Mintage	Fine	VF	EF	UNC/BU
1838	P1553	591,360	£5	£12	£40	£140/
1838*	P1553	DEF. full stop	£10	£30	£100	
1839	P1554	4,300,800	£4	£12	£40	£140/
1839	ND	'DEF' no stop	£10	£25	£100	£350/
1839	ND	Two-pronged trident		£200	£300/£400	
1840	P1559	3,010,560	£3	£15	£50	£140/
1840	ND	Two-pronged trident	£80		£200	
1840*	ND	'DEF.' variety	£10	£30	£100	
1841	P1560	1,720,320	£4	£10	£50	£140/
1841	ND	Inverted 'V's for 'A's in GRATIA		£200 (2009)		
1841	ND	As above + dot in 1st 'A' of Britannia VF: £100 (2009)				
1841	ND	Varieties - REG. and REG for REG:				£200/
1842	P1562	1,290,240	£12	£50	£120	£300/
1842	ND	Large '42'	£30	£80	£200	
1843	P1563	4,085,760	£4	£10	£50	£100/£150
1843	P1564	1 for 1 in date			£600	£1500/
1843	ND	3 over 2		£90	£250	
1844	P1565	430,080	£50	£150	£600	£2200/£2500
1845*	P1566	(A)	£10	£20	£60	£120/£200
1845*	ND	3,225,600 (B)	£12	£25	£70	£160/£250
1845	ND	Larger date	£90	£180		
1846	P1567	2,580,480	£10	£20	£50	
1847	P1568	3,879,720	£5	£10	£50	£130/
1848	P1569	1,290,246	£5	£10	£60	£130/

Victoria 1857 (Young Head) Farthing

*1838 variety DEF. has just one dot where there should be a colon.
*1840 variety DEF.. has two horizontal dots where there should be a colon.
*1845 Type A has a normal straight '8'. Type B has an '8' which leans to the left.

VICTORIA Young head. Copper 22mm. Weight 4.7g (continued)

Date	Peck	Mintage	Fine	VF	EF	UNC/BU
1849	P1570	645,120		£50	£100	£300	
1850	P1571	430,080 ?	£4	£10	£60	£100/
1850	ND	5 over inverted 5 or 3??		£40		£200/
1850	ND	5 over 4		£30	£150	£200/
1850	ND	Inverted 'V's for 'A's in Britannia			£150	
1851	P1572	1,935,360	£10	£25	£70	£150/
1851	P1573	D of 'DEI' struck over sideways 'D'			£300	
1852	P1574	822,528	£10	£25	£100	£150/
1853	P1575	1,028,628 W.W. raised	£4	£10	£50	£120/
1853	ND	3 over 2, raised W.W.		£10	£50	
1853	P1578	WW incuse	£5	£20	£80	£200/
1853	ND	Inverted V's for A's in BRITANNIA. VF: £150				
1854	P1580	6,504,960	£5	£10	£40	£100/
1855	P1581	3,440,640 WW incuse		£15	£50	£120/
1855	P1582	W.W. raised		£10	£50	£100/
1856	P1583	1,771,392	£7	£20	£50	£100/
1856*	P1584	E over R in Victoria	£25	£50	£100	£300/
1857	P1585	1,075,200	£5	£15	£50	£100/
1858	P1586	1,720,320	£5	£15	£50	£120/
1858	ND	Small date	£50	£120		
1859	P1587	1,290,240	£10	£30	£70	£180/
1860	P1588	Obverse date, copper type				£10,000 ?
1864	P1589	Obverse date. copper type				Ext. rare ?

*1856 E/R in VICTORIA. Also described as R over E. Either R was struck
over an incorrect E, or E was wrongly selected to improve a poor R; (or ?)

Farthings from this point onwards were struck in bronze (95% copper, 4% tin and 1% zinc until 1923).
Bronze was considered better than copper as it was more durable and wore at a slower rate. The coins
were also made in more convenient sizes. The bun head Victorian farthing dies were engraved by Leonard Charles Wyon.

VICTORIA Bun head. Bronze 20mm. Weight 2.84g

Date	FMAN	Mintage	Fine	VF	EF	UNC/BU
BB = Border of Beads. TB = Toothed Border						
1860		2,867,200 with various minor varieties, some rarer:				
1860	496	BB, 3 berries	£3	£8	£30	£100/
1860*	498	Beaded/toothed mule	£100	£300	£700	
1860	ND	Inverted reverse		(Cooke 2006) £500/		
1860	499	TB, 4 berries	£1	£3	£25	£80/
1860	501	TB, 5 berries	£1	£3	£25	£80/
1861	502	8,601,600. 4 berries	£2	£5	£25	£80/
1861	503	5 berries	£3	£5	£25	£80/
1861	ND	Date has small '8'	£3	£8	£30	£150/
1862	507	14,336,000	£4	£10	£40	£150/
1862	ND	Large fat '8'			£300	
1862	ND	Small '8' over large '8'		£100		
1863	509	1,433,600	£25	£50	£200	£350/
1863	ND	Dot below lighthouse	(Cooke 2006)		£400/	
		(London Coins 2007)	GVF: £90			

Victoria 1860 toothed rim Farthing

VICTORIA Bun head. Bronze 20mm. Weight 2.84g (continued)

Date	FMAN	Mintage	Fine	VF	EF	UNC/BU
1864	511A	2,508,800 serif 4*	£5	£12	£50	£100/
1864	511	plain 4*	£2	£6	£30	£90/
1865	512	4,659,200	£2	£5	£35	£90/
1865	513	5 over 2	£3	£10	£50	£120/
1865	ND	5 over 3	£4	£10	£50	£120/
1865	ND	Date has small '8'	£2	£8	£35	£100/
1866	514	3,584,000	£1	£10	£50	£140/
1866	ND	RFG for REG (broken die)		£20	£60	£200/
1866	ND	widely spaced 6's	£3	£20	£70	£200/
1867	516	5,017,600	£2	£10	£60	£150/
1868	519	4,851,208	£2	£6	£40	£130/
1869	522	3,225,600	£5	£20	£60	£150/
1872	523	2,150,400	£4	£10	£40	£100/
1873	524	3,225,620	£2	£6	£40	£100/
1873	ND	Low set 3 in date	£4	£20	£80	£200/
1874H	525	3,584,000	£2	£10	£50	£120/
1874H	527	G's struck over sideways G's			£500	
1875	528	Large date (5 berries)	£6	£30	£40	
1875	529	Small date (4 berries)	£10	£40	£150	£300/
1875H	530	Small date (5 berries) with Full rose brooch visible on bodice. Extremely Rare, and not to be confused with the very common slightly aged obverse type below. VF: £400				
1875	531	712,760 (for more '1875' details see Freeman book)				
1875H	532	Small date, 4 berries	£10	£25	£70	£150/
		6,092,800, 4 berries	£1	£3	£30	£90/
1875H	ND	5 over 2 noted 1999			£50	
1875H	ND*	R.F.G for REG	£8	£20	£80	£180/

* A fairly common die break.

Date	FMAN	Mintage	Fine	VF	EF	UNC/BU
1876H	534	1,175,200	£5	£10	£40	£100/
1876H	534A	Large 6 in date	£10	£30	£90	£150/
1876H	ND*	RF.G for REG die break	£5	£25	£75	£180/£240
1877		Proof Only				
1878	536	4,008,540	£1	£3	£25	£80/
1879	538	3,977,180	£4	£10	£25	£80/£120
1879	540	Date has large '9'	£10	£30	£75	£200/
1880	541	1,842,710 (4 berries)	£1	£5	£30	£100/
1880	543	(3 berries)	£10	£60	£120	£200/
1881	544	4 berries (incl. below)		£100		
1881	545-6	3,494,670. 3 berries	£2	£7	£30	£100/
1881H	548	1,792,000	£1	£5	£50	£120/
1881H	ND	H further to left			£250	
1882H	549	1,790,000	£2	£5	£30	£100/
1883	551	1,128,680	£3	£8	£40	£100/
1884	553	5,782,000	£1	£3	£30	£100/
1885	555	5,442,308	£1	£3	£30	£100/
1886	557	7,767,790	£1	£4	£30	£100/
1887	559	1,340,800	£1	£4	£30	£100/
1888	560	1,887,250	£1	£4	£30	£80/
1890	562	2,133,070	£1	£4	£30	£80/
1891	564	4,959,690	£1	£4	£25	£75/

*1864 - Plain and serif '4' in date: See the penny section for more details.

'H' centered below date = Heaton Mint (Coin was not made at the Royal Mint)

All Royal Mint coins 1875 to 1878 have an 'R' with a forked tail; the Heaton Mint issues do not. So an 1875 with forked 'R' might well be an 1875H with 'H' removed to Increase value!

During the 35 year run of bun-head farthings, minor changes were occasionally made to age the queens portrait

Minor die varieties of 1881H Farthings occur, but a whole book would be needed to point out the intricate but very minor differences!

VICTORIA Bun head. Bronze 20mm. Weight 2.84g (continued)

Date	FMAN	Mintage	Fine	VF	EF	UNC/BU
1892	566	887,240	£5	£10	£50	£150/
1893	568	3,904,320	£1	£4	£25	£75/£90
1893	ND	Narrower date	£2	£8	£40	£150/
1894	569	2,396,770	£1	£7	£25	£75/£100
1895	570	2,852,853	£10	£20	£75	£150/

The veiled head Victoria portrait was engraved by George William de Saulles, from a Model by Thomas Brock. The reverse was also the work of de Saulles. Most of the 1897 farthings, and all farthings up to 1917 were chemically darkened to avoid them being confused for half sovereigns, which were of a very similar size.

VICTORIA Old or widow head. Bronze 20mm. Weight 2.86g

Date	FMAN	Mintage	Fine	VF	EF	UNC/BU
1895	571	Incl. with bun head	£1	£3	£10	£30/£40
1896	572	3,668,610		£2	£8	£40/
1897	ND	Bright finish			£10	£40/£60
1897		4,579,800 Blackened.				
1897*	574	Horizon as 1896	£1	£3	£10	£40/£50
1897**	575	Higher horizon	£1	£3	£10	£40/£50
1898	576	4,010,080		£2	£8	£30/£40
1899	577	3,864,616		£1	£8	£40/£55
1900	578	5,969,317		£2	£8	£25/£40
1901	579	8,016,459		£1	£5	£20/£25
1901	ND	Bright finish error				/£100

* = The '7' points to a border tooth. ** = The '7' points between two teeth

Victoria 1897 Farthing

George William de Saulles also engraved the dies for the Edward VII farthings. The reverse remained very similar to the previous Victorian farthings.

EDWARD VII Bronze 20mm. Weight 2.83g

Date	FMAN	Mintage	Fine	VF	EF	UNC/BU
1902	580	5,125,120. A		£2	£10	£25/£30
1902	ND	Incl above. B		£2	£10	£30/£40
1903	581	5,331,200	£1	£4	£12	£30/£40
1904	582	3,628,800	£1	£4	£15	£25/£30
1904	ND	Bright finish error			£80/	
1905	583	4,076,800		£4	£15	£30/
1906	584	5,340,160		£3	£15	£30/£40
1907	585	4,399,360		£2	£10	£30/
1908	586	4,264,960		£4	£10	£25/£30
1909	587	8,852,480		£2	£10	£25/£30
1910	588	2,598,400	£1	£4	£15	£25/£30

Edward VII 1904 Farthing. All
Edward VII farthings were
Chemically darkened.

Type A: Weak strike - patchy breastplate on Britannia.
Type B: Well struck - clear design work.

Farthings of George V, VI and Elizabeth II

The portrait of George V was the work of Sir Bertram Mackennal. The reverse was a slightly altered version of the Edward VII reverse type. The farthings of George VI saw a departure from the traditional designs of former years, and a Wren by H Wilson Parker was chosen to be used as a new reverse type. The George VI portrait was the work of Thomas Humphrey Paget. The bust of Elizabeth II was the work of Mary Gillick and the Wren reverse was the same as that used previously.

GEORGE V Bronze 20mm. Weight 2.82g

Date	FMAN	Mintage	VF	EF	UNC/BU
1911	589	5,196,800 *Ia	£2	£8	£20/£30
1911	ND	*Ib (see right)	£3	£10	£25/£35
1912	590	7,669,760		£4	£15/£18
1913	591	4,134,320		£3	£15/£18
1914	592	6,126,988 BRITT Obv.1		£8	£24/£30
1914	593	BRIT_T (gap)		£8	£20/£30
1915	593A	BRITT (no gap)			£250/£350
1915	594	7,129,254 BRIT_T	£1	£10	£35/
1916	595	10,993,325		£3	£15/
1917	596	21,434,844		£2	£15/
1918	597	19,362,818 Bright			£15/
1918	ND	Scarcer, darkened surface		£10	£25/
1919	598	15,089,425		£2	£10/£15

George V 1921 Farthing

*1911 - Obv Ia: Above B.M. the neck is hollow.
Obv Ib: Above B.M. the neck is flat.

1914 & 1915:
Varieties with different spacing between the
T's in BRITT occur. BRITT represents close
spacing, and BRIT_T represents far spacing.

GEORGE V Bronze 20mm. Weight 2.82g (continued)

Date	FMAN	Mintage	VF	EF	UNC/BU
1919	598	15,089,425		£2	£10/£15
1920	599	11,480,536		£2	£10/£15
1921	600	9,469,097		£2	£10/£15
1922	601	9,956,983		£2	£10/£15
1923	602	8,034,457		£3	£10/£20
1924	603	8,733,414		£2	£10/£14
1925	604	12,634,697		£5	£14/£20
1926	605	9,792,397 New Obv/Rev from here		£1	£12/
1927	607	7,868,355		£1	£12/
1928	609	11,625,600		£1	£8/£12
1929	611	8,419,200		£1	£10/£15
1930	613	4,195,200		£1	£10/£12
1931	615	6,595,200		£1	£8/£12
1932	617	9,292,800		£1	£10/£12
1933	619	4,560,000		£1	£8/£12
1934	621	3,052,800		£3	£8/£15
1935	623	2,227,200	£2	£5	£15/£20
1936	625	9,734,400		£1	£5/£10

EDWARD VIII

Date	FMAN	Mintage	UNC/BU
1937	627	Extremely rare (not issued for general circulation)	

GEORGE VI Bronze 20mm. Weight 2.84g

Date	FMAN	Mintage	UNC/BU
1937	628	8,131,200	£3/£5
1937	629	26,402 Proofs	£5/£8
1938	630	7,449,600	£6/£10
1939	632	31,440,000	£5/£7
1940	634	18,360,000	£5/£7
1941	636	27,312,000	£5/£7
1942	638	28,857,600	£5/£7
1943	640	33,345,600	£5/£7
1944	642	25,137,600	£5/£7
1945	644	23,736,000	£5/£7
1946	646	23,364,800	£5/£7
1947	648	14,745,600	£5/£7
1948	650	16,622,400	£5/£7
1949	652	8,424,000	£5/£7
1950	654	10,324,800	£5/£7
1950	655	17,513 Proofs	£10/£14
1951	656	14,016,000	£6/£10
1951	657	20,000 Proofs	£10/£14
1952	658	5,251,200	£7/£10

George VI 1943 Farthing

ELIZABETH II Bronze 20mm. Weight 2.85g

Date	FMAN	Mintage	EF	UNC/BU
1953		6,131,037 :		
	660	Obverse 1 Reverse A, From set		£5/£7
	661	Obverse 1 Reverse B	£2	£15/£25
	662	Obverse 2 Reverse A	£3	£20/£30
	663	Obverse 2 Reverse B		£3/£7
	664	40,000 Proofs		£5/£7
	662A	Proof Obverse 2 + Reverse A		£70/£100
1954	665	6,566,400		£3/£5
1955	667	5,779,200		£3/£5
1956	669	1,996,800	£2	£10/£15

Elizabeth II 1954 Farthing. The wren type reverse was also used for the farthings of Elizabeth II

Obverse 1: Is poorly defined. The cross points TO a border bead.
Obverse 2: Is sharper. The cross points BETWEEN two border beads.
Reverse A: (uses the dies of George VI) - The 'F' points BETWEEN two beads.
Reverse B: Is similar, but the 'F' points TO a border bead.

1953 Obverse/Reverse Rarity Scale 1 + A is scarce. 2 + A is rare. 1 + B is rare.
2 + B is very common.

Halfpennies

This was the first issue of halfpennies under George III. See also the introduction to the 1771-5 farthings regarding mintage numbers. The halfpennies were also melted down in very large numbers, the copper being used to make lightweight counterfeits. It was a big problem at the time and wasn't really solved until the introduction of the Boulton coin presses in the late 1790s. A genuine halfpenny should weigh between just over 9 grammes to just under 11 grammes. These were not struck with a collar, so are not perfectly round. The diameter varies from about 28.5mm to 30mm. Most of the lightweight counterfeits are fairly inexpensive and still very common. Some however, can actually be just as collectable as the real ones - in fact certain types of counterfeit halfpennies with an American connection are very rare and sought after.

GEORGE III Copper, about 30mm. Weight 9.9g (average)

Date	Peck	Notes	Fine	VF	EF
1770	P893		£10	£50	£180
1770	P893A	No stop on reverse	£15	£60	£250
1771	P896		£10	£50	£180
1771	P897	No stop on reverse	£15	£60	£250
1771	P898	Ball below spear head	£12	£50	£200
1772	P899	Reverse A*	£10	£50	£180
1772	P900	GEORIVS error	£30	£100	£400
1772	P901	Ball below spear head	£10	£50	£180
1772	P902	Reverse B*	£10	£50	£150
1772	P903	No stop on reverse	£15	£60	£200
1773	P904		£10	£50	£180
1773	P905	No stop after REX	£10	£50	£180
1773	P906	No stop on reverse	£25	£100	£300
1774	P907		£10	£50	£180
1775	P908		£10	£50	£180

* There were actually three slightly different reverses used on 1770-5 halfpennies. 1772 is the only date for which two different types occur, both are quite common. Reverse A: Britannia has an incuse curl of hair on the top of her head. The scroll at the base of the shield has curved raised lines. Reverse B: No coil of hair on the top of Britannia's head. The scroll has straight incuse lines.

George III 1771 Halfpenny.
Reproduced from a Victorian
publication,.

The 1799 halfpenny was the next official halfpenny issue after 1775. Following on from the successful introduction of the Cartwheel Twopence and Penny in 1797, Matthew Boulton also produced the 1799 and 1806/07 Halfpennies. The dies were prepared by Conrad Heinrich Küchler.

GEORGE III Soho Mint, Copper 31mm. Weight 12.66g

Date	Peck	Mintage	Fine	VF	EF	UNC/BU
1799	P1248	5 incuse ship gunports	£3	£10	£60	£200/
1799	P1249	6 raised ship gunports	£3	£8	£50	£180/
1799	P1250	9 raised ship gunports	£3	£8	£50	£180/
1799	P1251	Plain ship hull	£5	£20	£70	£180/
1799	P1252	Raised line on ship, no guns	£3	£15	£60	£180/

2nd type, Soho Mint, Copper 29mm. Weight 9.43g

Date	Peck	Mintage	Fine	VF	EF	UNC/BU
1806	P1376	Olive branch no berries	£5	£10	£60	£150/
1806	ND	Ball under trident prongs, which is normally only seen on the proof varieties. Reported on predecimal.com 2006.				
1806	P1377	3 berries 'SOHO' *	£5	£10	£50	£150/
1807	P1378	3 berries 'SOHO' *	£5	£10	£50	£150/

* The word SOHO is underlined on the reverse of the coin.

1799 Soho Halfpenny

1806 Soho Halfpenny

The copper halfpennies of George IV, William IV and Victoria are all the work of William Wyon (the portrait of William IV was based on a model by Sir Francis Chantry). The reverse type remained the same until 'REG' replaced 'REX' for the issues struck under Queen Victoria.

GEORGE IV Laureate head, Copper 28mm. Weight 9.34g

Date	Peck	Mintage	Fine	VF	EF	UNC/BU
1825	P1431	215,040	£12	£30	£150	£300/
1826	P1433	9,031,630, Rev A	£6	£20	£70	£200/
1826	P1436	Rev B	£8	£30	£100	£250/
1827	P1438	5,376,000	£7	£25	£80	£200/

1826: Rev A: The saltire of shield has two incuse lines. Rev B: The saltire of shield has one raised line.

The saltire/St. Andrew's cross, is often divided by lines. More info about the St.Andrews cross and similar varieties can be found in the George IV penny section.

WILLIAM IV Bare head, Copper 28mm. Weight 9.39g

Date	Peck	Mintage	Fine	VF	EF	UNC/BU
1831	P1461	806,400	£15	£40	£100	£250/
1834	P1464	537,600	£12	£25	£100	£250/
1837	P1465	349,400	£12	£25	£100	£300/

VICTORIA Young head with date below, Copper 28mm. Weight 9.46g

Date	Peck	Mintage	Fine	VF	EF	UNC/BU
1838	P1522	456,960	£6	£15	£70	£200/
1841	P1524	1,075,200	£5	£12	£60	£200/
1841	ND	Broken die: DEI reads DF.I			£100	
1841	ND	Alignment Up/down (Ap I)	£20	£50	£200	
1843	P1527	967,680	£50	£100	£300	£600/
1844	P1528	1,075,200	£10	£20	£100	£200/
1845	P1529	1,075,200	£200			
1846	P1530	860,160	£10	£30	£120	£300/
1847	P1531	752,640	£10	£30	£120	£300/
1848	P1533	322,560	£30	£80	£200	£500/

George IV 1826 Halfpenny

William IV 1837 Halfpenny

On the next page some of the 1850s halfpennies have either no dots near the shield (left image) or 7 incuse dots on and around the shield (right image)

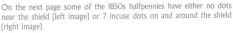

VICTORIA Young head with date below (continued)

Date	Peck	Mintage	Fine	VF	EF	UNC/BU
1848	P1532	8 struck over 7	£6	£20	£100	£250/
1848	ND	8 struck over 3	£5	£20	£100	
1851	P1534	215,040 no dots on				
		or above shield*		£20	£100	
1851	P1535	Shield, 7 incuse dots*	£6	£10	£50	£200/
1852	P1536	637,056 (no dots)*	£5	£10	£60	£220/
1852	P1537	Shield, 7 incuse dots*	£6	£10	£60	£200/
1853	P1539	1,559,040	£3	£12	£50	£200/
1853	P1538	3 over 2		£20	£80	£250
1854	P1542	12,354,048 ?	£4	£10	£40	£100/
1855	P1543	1,455,837	£4	£10	£40	£100/
1856	P1544	1,942,080	£4	£10	£40	£150/
1856	ND	6 over larger 6 (values perhaps a little more than above)				
1857	P1545	Shield, 7 incuse dots*	£5	£10	£50	£120/
1857	P1546	1,182,720 (no dots)*	£7	£10	£40	£150/
1858	P1549	2,472,960	£5	£10	£60	£120/
1858	ND	Smaller date	£5	£15	£60	£120/
1858	P1547	Last 8 over 6	£5	£15	£60	£120/
1858	P1548	Last 8 over 7	£5	£12	£60	£120/
1859	P1551	1,290,340	£8	£15	£60	£150/
1859	P1550	9 struck over 8	£6	£20	£80	£200/
1860*	P1552	Extremely rare	£500	£2000	£5000	

*Copper type - Date is below head, not below Britannia.

Victoria 1853 Halfpenny

*For an illustration of the no dots and seven dots varieties, see previous page.

In 1860 the first halfpennies were produced in bronze. For these and the other 'coppers' an alloy comprising 95% copper was chosen. The dies were the work of Leonard Charles Wyon. Massive demands were made on the Royal Mint and as a result some bun head farthings were struck by private mints in Birmingham, to ease the workload.

VICTORIA 'Bun' head, date on reverse, Bronze 26mm. Weight 5.69g

Beaded Borders:

Date	FMAN	Mintage	Fine	VF	EF	UNC/BU
1860	258	Obv 1	£3	£10	£40	£100/
(Freeman 258 has 2 slightly different reverses, distinguishable						
by the differences in the length of Britannia's hair)						
1860	260A	Obv 1*			£100	£250/
1860	260C	Mule toothed/beaded borders (Coincraft 1995) £1000				

Toothed borders:

1860	261	Obv 2, Rev B	£10	£40	£100	£300/£400
1860	264	Obv 2, Rev C	£3	£15	£70	£200/
1860	265	Obv 3, Rev B	£2	£8	£80	£250/
1860	266	Obv 4, Rev B	£4	£12	£80	£250/
1860	267	Obv 4, Rev C	£2	£10	£70	£200/
1860	ND	F of HALF over P	£250			
1861 - 12 minor varieties occur, most dealers do not distinguish.						
1861	269-82	54,118,400	£3	£8	£90	£200/
1861	274A/82A	6 over 8	£1000 (Fine)			
1861	279	Last 1 over lower 1 reported on predecimal.com forum.				
1861	ND	R over B in BRITT.	NF: £178 (2007) See opposite.			

Obv 1 has 6 berries in the wreath arranged in pairs. Obv 1* is as Obv 1 with minor changes - the knot in the hair tie has been removed. Obv 2 has 7 berries. Obv 3 has 5 berries. Obv 4 has 4 berries.

Reverse types: B - lighthouse tapering, pointed. C - lighthouse cylindrical with rounded top. Some 1861 Bun head Halfpennies bear F's with little or no lower serif to the lower horizontal bar.

1861 Halfpenny detail showing the R over B in BRITT. First made public on the Predecimal.com forum by Gary Brett. So far only one is known.

AJW COINS

VICTORIA 'Bun' head, Bronze 26mm, Weight 5.69g (continued)

Date	FMAN	Mintage	Fine	VF	EF	UNC/BU
1862	289	61,107,200	£2	£6	£50	£150/
1862	289A	A to left of lighthouse. 2014 London Coins NVF: £700				
1862	288	B to left of Lighthouse. VG: £440 (2014)				
1862	288A	C to left of Lighthouse. VG: £280 (2014)				
1862	290A	Unbarred A left of lighthouse. VF: £600 (2013)				
1863	292	15,948,800	£2	£8	£75	£200/
1863	294	With smaller straighter '3'.		£20		£300/
1864	295	537,600	£4	£10	£70	£250/
1865	296	8,064,000		£20	£100	£400/
1865	297	5 over 3	£35	£100	£350	£750/
1866	298	2,508,800	£5	£20	£80	£250/
1867	300	2,508,806	£5	£15	£80	£300/
1868	303	3,046,400	£5	£15	£75	£250/
1869	306	3,225,600	£20	£100	£300	£1500/
1870	307	4,350,739	£5	£16	£70	£200/
1871	308	1,075,280 ?	£20	£100	£300	£850/
1872	309A	4,659,410	£5	£10	£60	£180/
1873	310	3,404,880	£5	£12	£80	£200/
1873	311	St. Andrews cross slightly out of line.				£250/
1874	312-317	1,347,665 16 Wreath leaves	£20	£60	£200	£300/
1874H	318	5,017,600	£5	£15	£60	£150/
1875	321-322A	5,430,815. MV	£5	£16	£70	£150/
1875H	323	1,254,400	£5	£15	£70	£200/
1876H	325-329	6,809,600. MV	£5	£15	£80	£200/
1877	330-334	5,209,505. MV	£5	£15	£70	£200/
1878	334/5/7	1,425,535. MV	£10	£30	£150	£400/
1879	338/9	3,582,545. MV	£6	£10	£60	£150/
1880	340/41A	2,423,465. MV	£2	£5	£50	£160/
1881	342/43A	2,007,515. MV	£4	£8	£50	£150/
1881H	344	1,792,000	£4	£8	£50	£160/
1882H	347	4,480,000	£4	£8	£40	£150/
1883	349	3,000,725. Brooch*	£4	£8	£40	£150/
1883	348/348A/351 Rose*. MV			£50	£100	£200/

Victorian Bun head 1888 Halfpenny

MV = Minor varieties exist. Varieties not generally distinguished by most dealers and specialist reading is required for further identification details.

*1863 - Varieties in the style of the '3' in the date. One has a larger upper section and both are thought to exist in approximately equal numbers.
*1883 - At the Queen's neckline is either a small brooch or a small rose. The brooch consists of a large oblong shape with 6 ovals surrounding it.

VICTORIA 'Bun' head, Bronze 26mm, Weight 5.69g (continued)

Date	FMAN	Mintage	Fine	VF	EF	UNC/BU
1884	352	6,939,580	£1	£8	£50	£150/
1885	354	8,600,574	£1	£8	£50	£150/
1886	356	8,586,155	£1	£8	£50	£150/
1887	358	10,701,305	£1	£6	£40	£150/
1888	359	6,814,070	£1	£6	£30	£150/
1889	360	7,748,234	£1	£5	£50	£150/
1889	361	9 over 8	£10	£50	£150	£300/
1890	362	11,254,235	£1	£6	£20	£90/
1891	364	13,192,260	£1	£5	£30	£90/
1892	366	2,478,335	£2	£10	£70	£150/
1893	368	7,229,344	£1	£5	£50	£120/
1894	369	1,767,635	£3	£10	£60	£150/

VICTORIA Old or widow head. Bronze 26mm. Weight 5.64g

The obverse for this issue was engraved by George William de Saulles from a model by Thomas Brock, whose initials appear under the shoulder. The reverse is a modified version of the Leonard Charles Wyon design, with the lighthouse and ship removed.

* The 1897 higher tide variety has a tide level with the folds in Britannia's robe. The normal tide type has a tide level with the bottom of the robe. The veiled head Victorian Halfpenny was very similar in style to the penny.

Date	FMAN	Mintage	Fine	VF	EF	UNC/BU
1895	370	3,032,154	£1	£3	£15	£50/£70
1896	371/2	9,142,500. MV	£1	£2	£10	£40/£50
1897	373	8,690,315	£1	£2	£10	£50/£60
1897	374	Higher tide *	£2	£10	£35	£70/£80
1898	375	8,595,180	£1	£3	£12	£50/
1899	376	12,108,001	£1	£3	£10	£50/
1900	377	13,805,190	£1	£2	£8	£25/£40
1901	378	11,127,360	£1	£2	£8	£30/£40

EDWARD VII Britannia Reverse, Bronze 26mm. Weight 5.67g

The obverse of this issue was also engraved by George William de Saulles. Initially the same reverse was used as previously.

Date	FMAN	Mintage	Fine	VF	EF	UNC/BU
1902	380	Low tide	£5	£50	£120	£300/
1902	381	13,672,960 High tide		£2	£10	£30/£40
1903	382	11,450,880		£2	£15	£75/
1904	383	8,131,200	£3	£6	£20	£100/
1905	384	10,124,800		£5	£20	£80/
1906	385	11,101,440		£3	£20	£80/
1907	386	16,849,280		£3	£12	£70/
1908	387	16,620,800		£3	£12	£70/
1909	388	8,279,040		£4	£12	£70/
1910	389	10,769,920		£2	£10	£60/

1905 Halfpenny

The Low Tide variety referred to above and in the Edward VII penny section may be determined thus: if the horizon meets Britannia at the point below the knee, where right and left legs cross; NORMAL tide is indicated. If, however, the horizon meets Britannia at a much lower point - nearer the hem of her drape - then a LOW TIDE variety has been detected. Comparison with a normal tide other date Edward VII coin makes it much easier to tell.

The BM initials on the truncation of George V stand for Bertram Mackennal, the designer of the George V bust. The first reverse type was identical to that used for Edward VII. Unlike the pennies, there are no 'H' or 'KN' halfpennies, instead, many of the blanks produced for George V halfpennies were made by private firms in Birmingham and struck as normal, at the Royal Mint. There were problems with 'ghosting' (the faint outline of one side appearing on the other side) for this issue throughout most of the reign. Despite the bronze alloy being changed in 1923 (to 95.5% copper, 3% tin and 1.5% zinc) and the head being modified in 1925, this problem was not completely solved until the issue of the smaller head type in 1928.

GEORGE V Britannia Reverse, Bronze 26mm. Weight 5.658g

Date	FMAN	Mintage	VF	EF	UNC/BU
1911		12,570,880			
	390	*Obverse 1a	£2	£7	£30/£50
1911	ND	*Obverse 1b	£3	£10	£70/£80
1912	391	21,185,920	£2	£8	£25/£40
1913	392	17,476,480	£2	£8	£30/£45
1914	393	20,289,111	£2	£8	£30/£45
1915	394	21,563,040	£5	£12	£40/£50
1916	395	39,386,143	£1	£12	£35/
1917	396	38,245,436	£1	£8	£30/£40
1918	397	22,321,072	£1	£8	£30/£40
1919	398	28,104,001	£1	£8	£30/£45
1920	399	35,146,793	£1	£8	£30/£40
1921	400	28,027,293	£1	£8	£28/£35
1922	401	10,734,964	£2	£12	£50/£60
1923	402	12,266,282	£1	£8	£28/£40
1924	403	13,971,038	£1	£10	£30/£40
1925	404	12,216,123 Head as for 1924	£1	£6	£30/£40
1925	405	Modified effigy as for 1926, see appendix 1			
			£3	£12	£35/£50
1926	406	6,712,306	£2	£6	£30/£40
1927	408	15,589,622	£1	£6	£25/£35
Smaller Head:					
1928	410	20,935,200	£1	£5	£25/£35
1929	412	25,680,000	£1	£10	£50/£60
1930	414	12,532,800	£1	£6	£20/£35
1931	416	16,137,600	£1	£6	£20/£30
1932	418	14,448,000	£1	£5	£20/£30
1933	420	10,560,000	£1	£5	£20/£30
1934	422	7,704,000	£1	£6	£25/£35
1935	424	12,180,000	£1	£3	£20/£30
1936	426	23,008,800	£1	£3	£12/£20

1911* Obverse 1a has a hollow neck.
Obverse 1b has a flat neck.

1911 & 1912: Some dies were punched with date close to line of exergue.
Small gap = Rev A.
Clear gap = Rev B.

Combinations:: 1a+A 1a+B 1b+A 1b+B.

Most dealers do not differentiate.

George V Halfpenny 1913

George V Halfpenny 1931
(Smaller head and modified Britannia)

EDWARD VIII Reverse Golden Hind ship, Bronze 26mm
1937   Excessively rare, impossible to value.

As with the farthings of George VI, the decision was taken to break from tradition and change the reverse on the halfpennies too. Both the obverse and reverse were designed by Thomas Humphrey Paget, whose initials appear to the right of the Golden Hind on the reverse.

GEORGE VI Reverse Golden Hind ship, Bronze 26mm. Weight 5.7g

Date	FMAN	Mintage	EF	UNC/BU
1937	429	24,504,000	£1	£5/£7
1937	430	26,402 proofs		£8/£10
1938	431	40,320,000	£1	£8/£10
1939	433	28,924,800	£2	£15/£18
1940*	437/8	32,162,400	£2	£15/£18
1940	435	Thin rim, short teeth		£10/£20
1941	439	45,120,000	£1	£8/£10
1942	441	17,908,800	£1	£7/£8
1943	443	76,200,000	£1	£6/£7
1944	445	81,840,000	£1	£7/£8
1945	447	57,000,000	£1	£7/£8
1946	449	22,725,600	£2	£10/£15
1947	451	21,266,400	£1	£7/£8
1948	453	26,947,200	£1	£7/£8

*1940: 3 varieties -
Type 1: 'L' points between beads and the 'P' points to a bead. Type 2: 'L' and 'P' point between beads. Type 3: The 'L' points to a bead (see 'Pointings', appendix 1)

These varieties are rarely distinguished, and the prices are usually the same for each.

From 1949 the title IND:IMP (Emperor of India) was removed due to the India of the British Raj becoming two independent states (India and Pakistan).

Date	FMAN	Mintage	EF	UNC/BU
1949	455	24,744,000	£1	£10/£15
1950	457	24,153,600	£2	£10/£12
1950	458	17,513 Proofs FDC		£12
1951	459	14,868,000	£3	£15/£25
1951	460	Proofs 20,000 FDC		£10
1952	461	33,278,400	£2	£20/£25

George VI Halfpenny 1945

Elizabeth II 1959 Halfpenny

The Golden Hind continued to be used as the reverse type on the Halfpennies of Elizabeth II. Mary Gillick designed the obverse portrait, and her initials appear on the centre of the truncation of the shoulder. The first coins issued in 1953 had a very low relief portrait and showed very little detail, particularly to the hair area. The obverse die was re-cut during 1953, leading to the two slight varieties for that year. In 1954 the BRITT:OMN (of all the Britons) title was removed due to the changing state of the British Empire.

ELIZABETH II Reverse Golden Hind ship, Bronze 26mm. Weight 5.658g

Date	FMAN	Mintage	EF	UNC/BU
1953		8,910,000:		
1953	463	Obverse 1		£3/£5
1953	464	Obverse 2		£1/£2
1953	465/A	40,000 Proofs. MV		£3/£6
1954	466/8	19,375,200.MV	£6	£20/£30
1955	469	18,465,600		£4/£5
1956	471-5	21,799,200.MV		£5/£6
1957	477	39,672,000		£2/£3
1957*	476	Calmer sea rev	£6	£25/£40
1958	479/80	66,331,200. MV		£2/£3
	481	Thicker rim, shorter teeth		£150/
1959	483	79,176,000		£2/£3
1960	485	41,340,000		£4/£5
1962	487	41,779,200		£2/£3
1963	489	42,720,000		£2/£3
1964	491	78,583,200		£1/£2
1965	492	98,083,200		£1/£2
1965	ND	Error N. Zealand Rev		?
1966	493	95,289,600		50p/£1
1967*	494	146,490,400 Normal rim		40p/£1
1967*	495	Wide rim BU 2011		/£2.00 (Predecimal.com)
1970	495A/B.	750,424 Proofs		MV/£3 (Predecimal)

*Total mintage for 1967 Includes 46,226,400 struck in 1968, dated 1967.

1953 - Obv 1: The lower relief head. The cross points between rim beads. Obv 2: Slightly sharper. The Cross points to a rim bead.

1967 - Wide Rim or normal rim:

The illustration above shows both rim types. Without a comparison the difference can be detected by looking at the 'I' in 'DEI'. The wide rim variety 'I' points between two rim beads, with the normal rim coin it points directly at a rim bead.

The top image to the right is the 1957 Calm sea variety. The bottom image is the normal 1957 with choppy sea.

Minor reverse varieties occur for the 1957 calm sea type:
1. The '7' points to a bead. 2. The '7' points to left of bead. 3. The '7' points to space. 4. A blunter '7' that points to a bead. Number 2 is thought to be the rarest.

Silver Pennies: See Maundy section.

Pennies
No official copper pennies were struck during the reign of George III until this issue, in 1797. From 1770 until the end of the 18th century the practice of melting down the official copper coins and making lightweight forgeries had become so widespread that it prompted industrialist Matthew Boulton to offer a potential solution. He proposed that each coin should actually be made to contain its value in copper and that the quality should be improved by using a retaining collar during striking (to give a perfectly round coin) and by designing the coins with thick raised borders to prevent them wearing so easily. Conrad Heinrich Küchler was the designer. By 1806 the price of copper had risen, and as a result the second Soho penny type was made of reduced weight. In fact, by the time they were ready, the price of copper had fallen and the intrinsic weight was less than the face value. The public accepted this, and ever since then, coins have been made with an actual metal value less than the face value.

George III 1797 Penny

* Varieties for 1797 concern the number of leaves in the Kings headdress.

GEORGE III First Soho 'Cartwheel' type, Copper 36mm. Weight 1oz/28.35g (official)

Date	Peck	Mintage	Fine	VF	EF	UNC/BU
1797	P1132	10 leaves*	£10	£40	£200	£600/
1797	P1133	11 leaves*	£10	£60	£250	£700/

George III 1807 Penny

GEORGE III Second Soho type, Copper 35mm. Weight 18.876g

Date	Peck	Mintage	Fine	VF	EF	UNC/BU
1806	P1342	Type A*	£6	£20	£80	£300/
1806	P1343	Type B*	£5	£20	£80	£400/
1807	P1344		£6	£20	£90	£350/
1808	P1346	One Known		Spink 1985	£15,000	
1808	"			Coincraft 1996	£35,000	

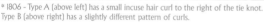
* 1806 - Type A (above left) has a small incuse hair curl to the right of the tie knot.
Type B (above right) has a slightly different pattern of curls.

George IV 1825 Penny

GEORGE IV Copper 34mm. Weight 18.72g.

Date	Peck	Mintage	Fine	VF	EF
1825	P1420	1,075,200 Type A	£12	£40	£200
1826	P1422	5,913,000 Type A	£10	£40	£180
1826	P1425	Inc above. Type B	£10	£40	£200
1826	P1427	Inc above. Type C	£12	£50	£200
1827	P1430	1,451,520 Type A	£200	£600	£3500

No pennies or halfpennies were issued from 1820 to 1824, and it was only when the new portrait by William Wyon was designed in 1825 (which the king much preferred) that an issue of pennies and halfpennies were made. The reverse was also the work of William Wyon.

Type A   Type B   Type C

The reverse varieties of the 1826 George IV pennies all concern slight differences to the cross of St. Andrew in the flag on the shield:
Rev A = No central line along arms of cross.
Rev B = Thin, raised line along cross.
Rev C = Thick, broad raised line along cross.
With many worn coins these varieties are impossible to differentiate, especially without a comparison.

William IV 1837 Penny

The portrait of King William IV was engraved by William Wyon, from a bust by Sir Francis Chantrey. The reverse was the same as that used for King George IV. Coins were also struck in 1832, 1835 and 1836, but were not dated as such.

WILLIAM IV Copper 34mm. Weight 18.85g

Date	Peck	Mintage	Fine	VF	EF	UNC/BU
1831	P1455	806,400 no WW	£20	£80	£250	£600/
1831	ND	WW with no Dots	? Exists			
1831	P1458	.W.W incuse on trunc	£40	£100	£300	£700/
1831	P1458	W.W incuse on trunc	£100			
1834	P1459	322,560	£25	£70	£350	£1000/
1837	P1460	174,720	£40	£150	£500	

trunc = truncation, the base of the monarch's neck.

The copper Victorian pennies were, like the previous, engraved by William Wyon, who was clearly kept quite busy by the relatively frequent change of British monarchs in the first half of the 19th Century. The only change to the reverse was to replace 'REX' with 'REG' (for Regina).

VICTORIA Young Head, date below head, Copper 34mm. Weight 18.82g

Date	Peck	Mintage	Fine	VF	EF	UNC/BU
1841	P1480	913,920 REG:	£30	£150	£400	
1841	P1484	No colon REG	£5	£20	£100	£400/
1843	P1486	483,830 colon REG:		£200	£1000	
1843	P1485	No colon REG		£250	£3000	
1844	P1487	215,040	£8	£20	£100	£350/
1845	P1489	322,560		£35	£150	£600/
1846	P1490	483,840 DEF_:		£30	£150	£400/
1846	P1491	DEF:		£40	£200	£500/
1847	P1492	430,080 DEF:	£7	£25	£150	£350/
1847	P1493	DEF_:	£7	£25	£120	£300/
1848	P1496	161,280	£7	£25	£100	£350/
1848	P1494	8 over 6	£20	£100	£400	
1848	P1495	8 over 7	£10	£30	£120	£350/
1849	P1497	268,800	£200	£500	£1500	£3000
1851	P1498	432,224 DEF_:	£10	£30	£120	£350/
1851	P1499	DEF:	£9	£25	£100	£300/
1853	P1500	1,021,440 DEF_:	£5	£20	£100	£250/
1853	ND	Narrow date			£150	£400/
1853	P1503	DEF:	£4	£20	£80	£250/
1853	P1504	PT	£15	£35	£150	£350/
1854	P1505	4 over 3	£50	£100	£200	£450/
1854	P1506	6,720,000 PT	£5	£18	£100	£250/
1854	P1507	OT	£9	£20	£90	£250/
1855	P1508	5,273,866 OT	£5	£15	£80	£250/
1855	P1509	PT	£5	£10	£70	£250/
1856	P1510	1,212,288 DEF: PT	£70	£200	£600	£2000/
1856	P1512	DEF_: OT	£80	£250	£700	£2000/
1857	P1514	752,640 DEF: PT	£8	£20	£140	£250/
1857	P1513	DEF_: OT	£8	£20	£100	£250/
1857	P1514	Smaller date PT	£10	£20	£120	£250/
1858		1,559,040:				
	P1515	2nd 8 over 3		£100	£200	
	ND	2nd 8 over 6		?		
	P1516	2nd 8 over 7	£15	£100	£300/	
	ND	2nd 8 over 9			£400/	
	P1517	Smaller date	£4	£20	£100	£300/
	P1518	Large date, no W.W.	£4	£20	£80	£250/£300
	ND	Large date over small date. VF: £36 (noted 2008)				
1859	P1519	1,075,200 Large date	£8	£25	£80	£250/
1859	ND	9 over 8	£10	£40	£150	
1859	P1519	Smaller date	£8	£30	£100	£300/
1860*	P1521	60 struck over 59		£1500	£2500 £5000/	

*NOT with date below Britannia, smaller bronze type.

Victoria 1853 Penny

DEF: = near colon
DEF_: = far colon
OT - ornamental trident
PT - plain trident

Plain trident coins have near colons.

From 1839 to 1851 all have Ornamental tridents.

An ornamental trident (right image) is shown in comparison to a Plain trident (left image). Notice the extra garnishing under the main prongs of the ornamental trident.

The images above also illustrate a near colon after DEF and the far colon (right image)

The 'Bun' Penny

Copper, when alloyed with very small quantities of tin and zinc produces a harder alloy called bronze. An alloy of 95% copper with tin and zinc was used to produce British 'coppers' from 1860 onwards, with small changes in the alloy, right up to and including the decimal coinage. The dies of these lighter, smaller 'bun' pennies were engraved by Leonard Charles Wyon, a son of William Wyon, who was actually born on the Royal Mint premises in 1826.

The early bun head series is possibly the most complicated coin series ever! As you can see, there are 17+ different types just for the circulation 1860 coin alone. Correct identification can be a problem with coins in lower grades. Illustrations of every single type would be beyond the scope of this book and readers are refereed to 'The Bronze Coinage of Great Britain' by Michael Freeman (also published by Rotographic) and 'The British Bronze Penny - Struck for use as currency 1860 - 1970' by Michael Gouby. The latter is available on Mr Gouby's website: www.michaelcoins.co.uk

The reverse type letters are strictly those specified by Freeman in 'The Bronze Coinage of Great Britain". Here is a brief outline of the major reverse types:

Reverse A = The crosses are outlined by close, double raised lines, Britannia's thumb does not touch cross. no rock to left of lighthouse. **Reverse B** = The crosses are outlined with treble incuse lines, Britannia's thumb touches cross of St. George, no rock to left of lighthouse. **Reverse C** = Similar to Rev. A, but cross outlines are thinner and wider apart. Small rock to the left of lighthouse. **Reverse D** = As Reverse C, but with minor modifications to rocks and sea and, of course, a toothed border. **Reverse E** = As Reverse D, but with L.C.W. incuse below the foot, and the rim of the shield is thicker. **Reverse F** = No L.C.W signature and a rounded top to the lighthouse. Reverse **G** = No L.C.W signature. The shield is slightly convex (all previous types are flat). Where the letter 'H' appears in the listings after the date, it indicates a Heaton mint coin, distinguished by a small 'H' under date of the coin.

Victoria 1862 Penny

The varieties and design of the Bronze Victorian pennies are described in exquisite detail, by Michael J. Freeman in his book 'The Bronze Coinage of Great Britain' and by Michael Gouby in his book 'The British Bronze Penny - Struck for use as Currency 1860 - 1970'.

Above is Reverse A. Note the double raised lines outlining the crosses and that Britannia's thumb doesn't touch the cross.

Reverse B. Note the treble raised lines outlining the crosses and that Britannia's thumb does touch the cross.

VICTORIA Bun Head, date below Britannia, Bronze 30.8lmm. Weight 9.442g
1860 Bronze Penny. Mintage: 5,053,440
Beaded rim (T1), Obverse: 'L.C.WYON' partly on truncation

Rev	FMAN	Mintage	Fine	VF	EF	UNC/BU
A	1		£80	£500		
A	ND	extra heavy flan (probably a proof)		£1200		
B	6		£40	£80	£220	£700/
C	7		£100		£500	£1200
Mule	8	bead obv/tooth rev. Poor: £500 (2017).				
Mule	9	tooth obv/bead rev. NVG £550 (2017).				
D	13	signature below shield	£20	£100	£400/	
E	14	signature below foot	£750			
D	10	signature below shield	£15	£80	£200/	
D	ND	N of ONE over sideways N		£500	£1000/	
D	ND	struck on heavy flan	£300			
D	15	signature below truncation	£20	£100	£250/	
D	16	no signature 15 leaves	£40	£150	£500/	
D	17	no signature 16 leaves	£50	£300		
D	ND	ONF PENNY variety: damaged 'E':				
			£20	£90	£250	£400/
	ND	Michael Gouby '1860T' (see bibliography) Fine: £200				
	ND	E over P in PENNY. Fine: £950. Only 1 known.				
1861 Mintage: 36,449,280						
D	18	Signature	£60	£300	£600	
F	20	No signature	£100			
D	21	LCW almost touches border, see Freeman. Poor: £300 (2017)				
D	22	Signature below	£7	£20	£80	£200/£300
G	25	No signature	£200			
D	26	No signature, 15 leaves	£25	£80	£120	£200/
D	29	No signature, 16 leaves	£10	£40	£120	£200/
G	30	6 over 8	£700			
G	33	No signature	£7	£25	£50	£100/

Above is the obverse type with 15 leaves (and 4 berries). When counting, use a good lens and don't forget the leaves below the strands of hair which are swept over the ear!

Reverse C. Very similar to Reverse A but with small rock to left of the lighthouse.

VICTORIA Bun Head, date below Britannia, Bronze 30.81mm (continued)

Date	FMAN	Mintage	Fine	VF	EF	UNC/BU
1862	38	With signature (refer to Freeman, see bibliography)				£4000/
1862	ND	2 of date over 1	Near Fine: £1050			
1862*	39	50,534,400	£2	£15	£65	£240/
1862	41	Date from halfpenny die (smaller): Good Fine: £1600 (Bamford 2006)				
1862	39A	8 over 6	£2000			
1863	42	28,062,720	£2	£15	£65	£150/
1863	45	'2' below date	£4000 (Bamford 2006)			
1863	46	'3' below date	£2400 (Bamford 2006)			
1863	47	'4' below date	Good: £2000 (Bamford 2006)			
1863	ND	'5' below date, only one known. Very very worn: £18,000				
1863	ND	'3' with shorter lower serif in date. £1350 (Bamford 2006)				
(See book: 'The British Bronze Penny'. More details in bibliography section.)						
1864*	49	3,440,646, Type A	£30	£100		
1864*	48	Inc above. Type B		£1500		
1865	50	8,601,600	£7	£30	£100	£450/
1865	51	5 over 3	£40	£150	£600	£1200/
1866	52	9,999,360	£10	£25	£90	£350/
1867	53	5,483,520	£12	£50	£200	£600/
1868	56	1,182,720	£12	£60	£300	£750/
1869	59	2,580,480	£180	£400	£2500	
1870	60	5,695,022	£7	£30	£200	£500/
1870	ND	Narrower date			£300	
1871	61	1,290,318	£60	£100	£700	
1872	62	8,494,572	£7	£20	£100	£200/
1873	63	8,494,200	£7	£20	£100	£250/
1874		4 varieties. Freeman 65, 67, 70 and 72. Valuations similar.				
		5,621,865	£12	£40	£150	£350/
1874H		4 varieties. Freeman 66, 68, 71 and 73.				
		6,666,240	Fine: £12-£30 VF:£50-£100 EF:£200-£300			
1875	80	10,691,040	£10	£40	£120	£300/
1875	82	Wider date, thicker trident	?			
1875H	85	752,640	£40	£300	£800	£2000/
1876H	87	11,074,560	£8	£25	£120	£250/
1876H	89	Narrower date	£3	£10	£70	£150/
1876H	ND	With missing 'H'	Fair: £230	(Bamford 2006)		
1877	90	Small, narrow date. Fair: £3100	(Bamford 2006)			
1877	91	9,624,747	£6	£20	£100	£240/
1878	94	2,764,470	£8	£30	£150	£450/
1879*	96	7,666,476. Type A	£20	£100	£300	
1879*	97	Inc above. Type B	£4	£15	£100	£200/
1879	98	Small date	£100			
1880*	99	3,000,831	£10	£40	£130	£400/
1881	102	2,302,261	£4	£18	£180	£450/
1881*	106	Portrait 'aged' further	£120	£400		
1881H	108	3,763,200	£4	£20	£75	£250/
1882H	111	7,526,400	£20	£40	£90	£200/
1882H	ND	2 over 1		£350		
1882	112	No H* NF/AF:	£2200 (London Coins 2014)			

* 1862 - a recently discovered and so far very rare 1862 penny has 'VICTORIA' spelled with a 'G', reading 'VIGTORIA'!

* 1864 types A and B concern the '4' in the date. Type A '4's have an upper pointing serif coming off the right side of the horizontal crossbar of the '4'. Type B '4's have a 'T' shaped end on the horizontal part of the '4'.

*1879 Type A/B pennies have minor obverse differences. One of the easiest to spot (on higher grade coins) is that Type B has double incuse lines for leaf veins, whereas Type A has just a single line.

*1880 Pennies either have rocks to the left of the lighthouse, or not. The image above shows rocks. Values are the same.

*The aged portrait of 1881 is difficult to spot with worn coins, the easiest method is to count the leaves in the wreath - the aged portrait has 15, the normal version has 17.

• Beware of 1882H coins so worn that the 'H' is worn away, and of coins that have had the 'H' deliberately removed.

VICTORIA Bun Head, date below Britannia, Bronze 30.8lmm (continued)

Date	FMAN	Mintage	Fine	VF	EF	UNC/BU
1883*	116/8	6,237,438	£6	£15	£50	£200/
1884	119	11,702,802	£3	£10	£50	£150/£200
1885	121	7,145,862	£3	£10	£40	£140/£190
1886	123	6,087,759	£3	£10	£40	£140/£190
1887	125	5,315,085	£4	£15	£40	£120/£200
1888	126	5,125,020	£5	£20	£50	£170/£220
1889	127	12,559,737 15 leaves	£5	£15	£50	£120/£190
1889	128	Narrow date 14 leaves in wreath			£45	£100/£180
1890	130	15,330,840	£3	£12	£30	£100/£150
1890	ND	Narrow date		£200		
1891	132	17,885,961	£2	£10	£40	£120/£180
1891	ND	Wide spaced date			£340/	
1892	134	10,501,671	£5	£15	£50	£150/£200
1892	ND	Narrow spaced date. Fair: £15				
1893	136	8,161,737	£2	£10	£40	£150/
1894	138	3,883,452	£6	£20	£50	£200/£300

*There are two 1883 varieties (FMAN 116 and 118) but most dealers do not distinguish. The easiest way to tell the difference is one has the 'RI' of BRITT joined at the bottom, the other doesn't.

Dies were engraved by George William de Saulles for the final Victoria veiled head issue. The obverse was copied from a model by Thomas Brock, and the reverse was a modified version of the Leonard Charles Wyon type.

VICTORIA Old or Widow Head, Bronze 30.8lmm. Weight 9.467g

Date	FMAN	Mintage	Fine	VF	EF	UNC/BU
1895	141	5,395,830 Rev B		£4	£20	£80/£150
1895*	139	Rev A	£10	£40	£350	£1000/
1896	143	24,147,156	£1	£5	£20	£50/£80
1897	145	20,756,620	£1	£3	£20	£40/
1897	147	Spot between O and N in ONE			£1000/	
1897*	148	Higher tide		£130	£500	£1000/
1898	149	14,296,836	£1	£6	£20	£70/£140
1899	150	26,441,069	£1	£4	£20	£60/
1900	153	31,778,109		£5	£15	£50/£60
1901	154	22,205,568	£2	£15	£35/£45	

1895 - Rev A: trident to the 'P' is 2mm. No sea behind Britannia and to the right of Britannia the tide is very low (see image above).

Rev B: trident to P is 1mm. Sea present behind (to left of) Britannia and the tide level to the right is higher.

Victoria Penny 1901

1897 - Right: The higher tide meets Britannia well above the hemline. The normal tide coin is illustrated.

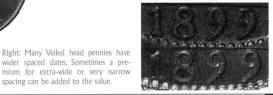

Right: Many Veiled head pennies have wider spaced dates. Sometimes a premium for extra-wide or very narrow spacing can be added to the value.

The dies for this issue were also by George William de Saulles ('De S' can be seen beneath the bust). Pennies struck early in 1902 used the same reverse as the veiled head Victoria issue. This die was slightly changed during 1902, resulting in the low tide, and normal tide types.

EDWARD VII Bronze 30.8Imm. Weight 9.435g

Date	FMAN	Mintage	Fine	VF	EF	UNC/BU
1902	156	Low tide	£6	£20	£100	£250/
		Minor date pointing varieties occur for the above.				
1902	157	26,976,768	£1	£3	£15	£40/£60
1903	158	21,415,296		£4	£20	£70/£90
1903	158A	Open '3' (bottom serif points at the 'O')				
					£100 (VG 2014) £1700 (GVF 2014)
1904	159	12,913,152		£8	£40	£100/£150
1905*	160/1	17,783,808		£5	£30	£90/£150
1906	162	37,989,504		£4	£20	£80/
1907	163	47,322,240		£4	£20	£80/
1908*	164-6	31,506,048		£5	£20	£80/
1909	168	19,617,024 'I' right of tooth			£30	£100/£150
1909	169	'I' is directly above a tooth: £800 (VG London Coins '14)				
1910	170	29,549,184		£4	£20	£75/£100

*1905 FMAN 160 and 161 either have upright part of the 'E' in 'PENNY' pointing at a rim bead or at a gap.

*1908 FMAN 164, 164A, 165 and 166 - Four slight varieties, most are common with the exception of 164A which has the colon after BRITT pointing to a rim tooth. This variety is rare.

Edward Penny 1902

The image above shows the 1902 low tide type; the tide is about level with the hemline. The image below shows the 1902 penny normal tide, which is higher and roughly level with where the legs cross.

George V 1918 Penny.
Large (first) head obverse.

The BM initials on the truncation of George V stand for Bertram Mackennal, the designer of the bust. The first reverse type was identical to that used for Edward VII. There were big problems with 'ghosting' (see also George V Half penny notes) for this issue throughout most of the reign. Despite the head being modified in 1926 and some changes to the reverse, this problem was not completely resolved until the issue of the smaller head type in 1928. The 1912, 1918 and 1919 H/KN pennies have the mintmark to the left of the date. Some 1912H pennies are 0.1mm greater in diameter.

GEORGE V Bronze 30.8Imm . Weight 9.45g

Date	FMAN	Mintage	Fine	VF	EF	UNC/BU
1911	171	23,079,168		£3	£20	£50/£60
1911	ND	'I' of BRITT points at tooth (Gouby X) Fine: £50-£100				
1912	172	48,306,048		£3	£20	£60/
1912H	173	16,800,000		£10	£70	£150/£250
1913*	174-7	65,497,872		£5	£30	£70/
1914	178	50,820,997		£10	£30	£55/
1915	179	47,310,807		£3	£20	£50/
1915 and 1916 with ear recessed, add approx 20%						
1916	180	86,411,165		£2	£20	£50/
1917	181	107,905,436		£2	£20	£50/
1918	182	84,227,372		£2	£20	£50/
1918H	183	3,660,800	£3	£25	£250	£500/
1918KN	184		£15	£70	£400	£800/
1919	185	113,761,090		£2	£20	£50/
1919H	186	5,209,600	£5	£50	£300	£850/
1919KN	187	Inc above	£20	£100	£600	£2000/
1920	188	124,693,485		£2	£20	£50/
1920	189	Colon after IMP points at a tooth. Ext. rare.				
1921*	190/1	129,717,693		£2	£20	£50/£60
1922	192	16,346,711		£3	£25	£40/£50
1922	192A	Centre trident prong well below tooth. Fine: £1200 (2006)				
1926	193	4,498,519		£10	£50	£150/
1926	195	Modified effigy, see app I	£30	£200	£1000	
1927	197	60,989,561		£2	£15	£40/
1928	199	50,178.000		£2	£15	£40/
1929	201	49,132,800		£1	£15	£30/
1930	203	29,097,600		£2	£20	£30/£40
1931	205	19,843,200		£2	£15	£40/£50
1932	207	8,277,600		£3	£30	£70/£100
1933*		7 or 8+ 'patterns'		£150k (2016)		
1933*		Pattern by Lavrillier, shown below - £72k (2016)				
1933*		A uniface £28,750 (1980)	?			
1933*		Modern reproduction fantasy 'patterns' are plentiful.				
1934	210	13,965,600		£2	£20	£50/£60
1935	212	56,070,000		£1	£5	£10/£20
1936	214	154,296,000		£1	£3	£10/£15

*1913 - Four minor varieties, all are fairly common and distinguishing them depends on the pointing of the 'P' on the reverse, and the position of the colon between 'GRA : BRITT'.

*1921 FMAN 190 and 191 - Two varieties occur, they can be differentiated by looking at the colon after 'DEF'. The 190 colon points to a gap, the 191 colon points to a tooth. Values are about the same.

*1933 Pennies shouldn't really be listed because none were struck for circulation. I thought I'd keep it here for completeness purely because it's probably the most legendary British penny ever!

George V 1935 Penny

George V 1933 Pattern Penny. Struck at the Royal Mint with dies by Frenchman André Lavrillier. It is thought there are only 4 in existence. The coin shown here is from the British Museum collection.

EDWARD VIII Bronze 30.8lmm

Date	FMAN	Mintage	VF	EF	UNC/BU
1937		Specimen strikings only			£50,000?

Edward VIII Penny from the British Museum Collection.

GEORGE VI Bronze 30.8lmm. Weight 9.442g

The obverse was engraved from a model by Thomas Humphrey Paget and the reverse was a slightly different Britannia type, modified by Royal Mint staff. During the war tin became scarce, so the percentage in the bronze alloy was reduced from 3% to 0.5%. The coins dated 1944 - 46 were also chemically darkened to give them the same tones as the previous un-treated coins. On all George VI coins, the titles IND:IMP were removed in 1949.

Date	FMAN	Mintage	Fine	VF	EF	UNC/BU
1937*	217/9	88,896,000			£1	£4/£8
1937*	218/20	26,402 Proofs			£3	£10/£15
1938	222	121,560,000			£1	£8/£12
1939	224	55,560,000			£2	£12/£20
1940	226	42,284,400		£3	£10	£30/£40
1940*	227	Double exergue line			£5	£20/£30
1944*	229	42,600,000			£3	£10/£20
1944*	ND	Not darkened by Mint				£20/£30
1945	231	79,531,200		£1	£5	£18/
1945	ND	Doubled 9		£5	£25	
1946	233	66,355,600			£2	£8/£10
1946	ND	Broken die, with high dot after 'ONE'		£50	£150/	
1947	235	52,220,400			£1	£4/£6
1948	236	63,961,200			£1	£3/£6
1949	238	14,324,400			£1	£4/£7
1950	240	240,000	£3	£8	£18	£50/£60
1950	241	17,513 Proofs				£30
1951	242	120,000	£3	£8	£25	£50/£60
1951	243	20,000 Proofs				£35
1952		(2006 Rasmussen)				£37,500

*1937 FMAN 217 and 219 - Two varieties occur with alternate pointings for the 2nd upright of the 'N' in 'ONE'. Both are fairly common and the same varieties are also found in the proof 1937 Pennies, FMAN 218 and 220.

*1940 FMAN 227. Below is an example of the double exergue 1940 penny

*1944 FMAN 229 - Unconfirmed sightings of a 1944 penny with the waves reaching slightly into the exergue.

George VI Penny first obverse with IND IMP.

George VI 1951 Penny

ELIZABETH II Bronze 30.8lmm. Weight 9.396g

Date	FMAN	Mintage	EF	BU
1953*	245	1,308,400	£3	£10
1953	246	40,000 Proofs		£18
1954		1 retrieved from change. Now in British Museum.		
1954		Another (2006 Rasmussen) £37,500		
1961	248	48,313,400		£3
1962	250	157,588,600		£2
1963	252	119,733,600		£2
1964	254	153,294,000		£1
1965	255	121,310,400		£1
1966	256	165,739,200		£1
1967	257	654,564,000**		50p
1970	257A	750,424 Proofs from the set		£6

* 1953 non proof pennies were only issued originally in the 9 coin plastic sets.
A very rare 1953 penny also exists (FMAN 243A) which was struck on a George VI
blank. It has a toothed obverse border and other slight differences.
** 1967 Mintage includes pennies minted in 1968, 69 and 70 but dated 1967.

Elizabeth II 1964 Penny

Three Halfpences (or One and a Half pence)

These tiny coins were issued for use in some colonies, and were never legal tender in the UK. They are included here because, like the fractional farthings, they are at the very least, relatives of the normal British Coinage, and they do bear the Latin word 'Britanniar' (Britain). I wonder how many of these tiddlers ended up down the back of chairs, never again to see the light of day.

WILLIAM IV .925 fine Silver 12mm. Weight 0.7g

Date	ESC	Mintage	Fine	VF	EF	UNC/BU
1834	2250	800,448	£5	£10	£40	£80/
1835	2251	633,600	£10	£20	£50	£120/
1835	2251A	5 over 4	£10	£20	£30	£100/
1836	2252	158,400	£5	£15	£40	£90/
1837	2253	30,624	£50	£200		

William IV 1834 Threehalfpence

VICTORIA .925 fine Silver 12mm. Weight 0.7g

Date	ESC	Mintage	Fine	VF	EF	UNC/BU
1838	2254	538,560	£6	£12	£30	£75/
1839	2255	760,320	£4	£12	£30	£75/
1840	2256	95,040	£8	£15	£70	£120/
1841	2257	158,400	£6	£15	£40	£90/
1842	2258	1,869,120	£4	£14	£40	£80/
1843	2259	475,200	£4	£12	£30	£60/
1843	2259B	43 over 34		£10	£60	£200/
1860	2260	160,000	£5	£20	£60	£120/
1862	2261	256,000	£5	£20	£60	£120/

Victoria 1839 Threehalfpence

Silver Twopences: See Maundy section.

Cartwheel Twopence

The heaviest British regal coin ever circulated, Cartwheel twopences are 41mm in diameter, over 5mm thick, and weigh almost 60 grammes each. With the Cartwheel Penny (see penny section) these two coins were the first to be struck for circulation by the new steam powered presses installed by James Watt at the premises of Matthew Boulton in Soho, Birmingham. The two men changed the shape (quite literally!) of British coinage and set the standard for all coins that followed. The fact they are such heavy coins means they are more likely to show signs of edge damage. Serious, or multiple edge knocks will result in lower values.

GEORGE III Copper 41mm. Weight 2oz/56.7g (official)

Date	Peck	Mintage	Fine	VF	EF	UNC/BU
1797	P1077	722,160	£25	£80	£300	£800/

George III Cartwheel Twopence

Threepences

George III, George IV and early William IV Threepences:
At some point in the late 1700s (the jury is still out on exactly when) the threepence stopped being a coin that was minted for circulation in large numbers, and was only minted for use in the annual Maundy ceremony. The circulation of a currency threepence for use in the United Kingdom was restarted in the early part of Queen Victoria's reign. For this reason, the threepences dated between 1762 - 1833 can be found in the Maundy section.

WILLIAM IV .925 fine Silver 16mm. Weight 1.414g

All the non-Maundy William IV threepences listed here were only issued for use in the West Indies. They do not have a prooflike mirror finish like the Maundy threepences.

Date	ESC	Details	Fine	VF	EF	UNC/BU
1831-1833 - Maundy type only see Maundy section.						
1834	2044	401,016	£7	£20	£90	£160/
1835	2045	491,040	£7	£20	£70	£160/
1836	2046	411,840	£7	£20	£70	£160/
1837	2047	42,768	£90	£250		

VICTORIA .925 fine Silver 16mm.. Weight 1.414g

Young Head, as Maundy type but without prooflike mirrored surface. The bust was changed slightly in 1859, 1867 and 1880, although some later coins were struck using earlier dies. A comprehensive listing of the four obverse types and two different reverses is given in 'English Silver Coins' by Maurice Bull.

Date	ESC	Details	Fine	VF	EF	UNC/BU
1838*	2048	1,203,840	£7	£18	£70	£150/
1838*	2048A	BRITANNIAB error			Extremely rare	
1839*	2049	570,240	£8	£20	£80	£200/
1840*	2050	633,600	£7	£20	£80	£200/
1841*	2051	443,520	£7	£28	£80	£200/
1842*	2052	2,027,520	£8	£20	£80	£200/
1843*	2053	Inc above	£7	£20	£80	£200/
1844*	2054	1,045,400	£5	£20	£80	£200/
1845	2055	1,314,720	£8	£20	£80	£150/
1846	2056	47,520	£150	£300	£500	£800/
1847*	ND	Unknown			£600	
1848*	2056A	Unknown			£500	£800/
1849	2057	126,720	£8	£20	£100	£300/
1850	2058	950,400	£7	£15	£80	£120/
1851	2059	479,065	£8	£15	£80	£150/
1851	2059A	5/8	£15	£40	£80	£150/
1852*	2059B		£60	£200	£500	£950/
1853	2060	31,680	£40	£100	£300	£500/
1854	2061	1,467,246	£7	£18	£100	£200/
1855	2062	383,350	£8	£25	£150	£250/
1856	2063	1,013,760	£8	£25	£80	£175/
1857	2064	1,758,240	£8	£25	£80	£175/
1858	2065	1,441,440	£7	£15	£60	£150/
1858	2065A	BRITANNIAB	£420 (VG London Coins 2014)			
1859	2066	3,579,840	£7	£15	£60	£110/
1860	2067	3,405,600	£7	£15	£60	£110/
1861	2068	3,294,720	£7	£15	£60	£120/
1862	2069	1,156,320	£10	£20	£70	£120/
1863	2070	950,400	£10	£25	£80	£150/
1864	2071	1,330,560	£7	£15	£60	£110/
1865	2072	1,742,400	£7	£20	£70	£140/

*Issued for colonial use only

Victoria Threepence 1864

VICTORIA .925 fine Silver 16mm.. Weight 1.414g [continued]

Date	ESC	Details	Fine	VF	EF	UNC/BU
1866	2073	1,900,800	£7	£15	£60	£110/
1866	2073	1,900,800	£7	£15	£60	£110/
1867	2074	712,800	£7	£15	£60	£110/
1868	2075	1,457,280	£7	£15	£60	£110/
1868	2075A	RRITANNIAR	£400			
1869	2075C	4,488 Maundy Only	£10	£25	£75	£200/
1870	2076	1,283,218	£5	£15	£50	£80/
1871	2077	999,633	£5	£15	£50	£80/
1872	2078	1,293,271	£10	£20	£60	£120/
1873	2079	4,055,550	£5	£12	£45	£80/
1874	2080	4,427,031	£5	£12	£45	£80/
1875	2081	3,306,500	£5	£12	£45	£60/
1876	2082	1,834,389	£5	£10	£45	£85/
1877	2083	2,622,393	£8	£15	£45	£85/
1878	2084	2,419,975	£10	£20	£50	£85/
1879	2085	3,140,265	£9	£15	£50	£85/
1880	2087	1,610,069	£6	£10	£40	£80/
1881	2088	3,248,265	£4	£9	£30	£70/
1882	2089	472,965	£10	£25	£70	£120/
1883	2090	4,365,971	£4	£10	£30	£70/
1884	2091	3,322,424	£5	£10	£35	£65/
1885	2092	5,183,653	£4	£10	£30	£60/
1886	2093	6,152,669	£4	£9	£30	£60/
1887	2094	2,780,761	£4	£10	£40	£75/

Victoria Young Head 1878 Threepence

The controversial Jubilee head bust (some remarked that it made the Queen look like a penguin, with a ridiculously small crown) was designed by Joseph Edgar Boehm.

VICTORIA .925 fine Silver 16mm Jubilee head (JH). Weight 1.414g

Date	ESC	Details	Fine	VF	EF	UNC/BU
1887	2096	Inc above	£2	£4	£6	£20/
1887	2097	Proof				£75/
1888	2098	518,199	£5	£10	£18	£45/
1889	2099	4,587,010	£2	£4	£15	£30/
1890	2100	4,465,834	£2	£4	£15	£30/
1891	2101	6,323,027	£2	£4	£15	£30/
1892	2102	2,578,226	£2	£5	£15	£30/
1893	2103	3,067,243	£15	£60	£160	£350/

Victoria Jubilee Head 1887 Threepence

Dies were engraved by George William de Saulles for the veiled head final Victoria issue. The obverse was copied from a model by Thomas Brock.

VICTORIA .925 fine Silver 16mm Old, or Widow head. Weight 1.414g

Date	ESC	Details	Fine	VF	EF	UNC/BU
1893	2104	Inc with JH	£2	£5	£10	£30/
1893	2105	1,312 Proofs				£100/
1894	2106	1,608,603	£3	£5	£18	£40/
1895	2107	4,788,609	£3	£5	£12	£40/
1896	2108	4,598,442	£3	£5	£12	£40/
1897	2109	4,541,294	£2	£4	£12	£40/
1898	2110	4,567,177	£2	£4	£12	£40/
1899	2111	6,246,281	£2	£4	£12	£35/
1900	2112	10,644,480	£2	£3	£10	£35/
1901	2113	6,098,400	£1	£4	£8	£35/

Victoria Veiled Head 1898 Threepence

EDWARD VII .925 fine Silver 16mm. Weight 1.414g
George William de Saulles engraved the Edward VII bust.

Date	ESC	Mintage	Fine	VF	EF	UNC/BU
1902	2114	8,268,480	£1	£2	£10	£20/
1902	2115	15,123 Proofs				£25/£35
1903	2116	5,227,200	£3	£8	£30	£40/
1904	2117	3,627,360	£6	£9	£35	£80/
1905	2118	3,548,160	£7	£11	£40	£80/
1906	2119	3,152,160	£3	£8	£30	£80/
1907	2120	4,831,200	£2	£5	£20	£40/
1908	2121	8,157,600	£2	£5	£15	£40/
1909	2122	4,055,040	£2	£8	£20	£50/
1910	2123	4,563,380	£1	£4	£15	£40/

Edward VII Threepence obverse.
Reverse type was as the early
George V Threepence (below)

GEORGE V .925 fine Silver 16mm. Weight 1.414g
The bust was by Bertram MacKennal, the reverse was carried over from the previous type until the acorn type was adopted in 1927, which was used up to the end of the reign.

Date	ESC	Mintage	Fine	VF	EF	UNC/BU
1911	2124	5,841,084	BV	£2	£7	£20/
1911	2125	6,001 Proofs				£25/
1912	2126	8,932,825	BV	£3	£9	£15/£20
1913	2127	7,143,242	£1	£4	£7	£20/£30
1914	2128	6,733,584	BV	£2	£6	£20/£25
1915	2129	5,450,617	BV	£2	£6	£20/£25
1916	2130	18,555,201	BV	£1	£4	£20/£25
1917	2131	21,662,490	BV	£1	£4	£20/£25
1918	2132	20,630,909	BV	£1	£4	£20/£25
1919	2133	16,845,687	BV	£1	£4	£20/£25
1920*	2134	16,703,597		£2	£6	£25/
Now debased .500 (50%) silver; type and size as previous.						
1920*	2135	.500 silver		£1	£5	£20/
1921	2136	8,749,301	£1	£3	£9	£25/
1922	2137	7,979,998	£1	£2	£20	£50/£70
1925	2138	3,731,859	£1	£5	£10	£40/£60
1926	2139	4,107,910	£1	£4	£30	£80/£100
1926	2140	Modified Effigy (Appendix I)	£4	£8	£30/	
1927	2141	15,022 Proofs			£50	£90/£110
1928	2142	1,302,106	£1	£4	£10	£30/
1930	2143	1,319,412	£2	£5	£15	£28/£40
1931	2144	6,251,936		£1	£5	£10/£14
1932	2145	5,887,325		£1	£5	£10/£14
1933	2146	5,578,541		£1	£3	£10/£12
1934	2147	7,405,954		£1	£2	£8/£10
1935	2148	7,027,654		£1	£2	£7/£9
1936	2149	3,238,670		£1	£2	£7/£9

George V Threepence 1920

* Sterling silver 1920 threepences have slightly stronger details, particularly on the serifs of the 'E's, owing to a slight difference in the resistance of the different alloys. Very difficult to spot, and good magnification is needed. Many dealers don't distinguish, as both are worth about the same.

George V Threepence,
2nd Reverse type (1927-1936)

EDWARD VIII

Date	ESC	Mintage	Fine	VF	EF	UNC/BU
1937	2149D	Pattern, 3 rings on reverse.		expensive!		

GEORGE VI .500 fine Silver 16mm. Weight 1.414g
New reverses were used for nearly all the George VI denominations. The silver threepence featured a St George's cross on a Tudor rose and was designed by George Kruger Gray, whose initials can be seen on many of the George VI reverses. The portrait was by Thomas Humphrey Paget.

Date	ESC	Mintage	Fine	VF	EF	UNC/BU
1937	2150	8,148,156			£2	£6/£7
1937	2151	26,402 Proofs				£8/£10
1938	2152	6,402,473			£3	£8/£10
1939	2153	1,355,860			£4	£15/
1940	2154	7,914,401			£3	£10/
1941	2155	7,979,411			£4	£12/
1942*	2156	4,144,051	£1	£6	£10	£30/
1943*	2157	1,379,220	£2	£5	£15	£40/
1944*	2158	2,005,553	£3	£10	£30	£70/
1945	2159	371,000	(1997: VF £4000)			

George VI Silver 1943 Threepence

Nearly all 1945 coins were melted down.
*For Colonial use only.

Threepences dodecagonal (12 sided) nickel-brass

EDWARD VIII

Officially, no coins bearing the portrait of Edward VIII were issued for circulation despite the fact that all the dies were prepared for all the denominations, and proofs were struck for approval. However, the brass threepence, being a new size and type was produced in slightly higher numbers, primarily for testing in vending machines. A handful of these coins were sent to vending machine manufacturers, and not all were returned! The obverse portrait was by Thomas Humphrey Paget and the reverse Thrift plant by Madge Kitchener. Normal thickness, and thinner varieties of this extremely rare coin are known to exist.

Date	Peck		UNC/BU
1937	2365/6	Date divided by THRIFT PLANT (Sea-pink); thicknesses vary. Cooke (1994)	£24,500
1937	2366	As George VI type but effigy of Edward VIII. Coincraft (1999)	£20,000

A current estimate would perhaps be £40,000+ for any type Edward VIII threepence. It's hard to say with any accuracy, as such a coin would most likely be auctioned and would generate very large interest.

Edward VIII Brass 1937 Threepence

GEORGE VI Nickel-brass, 12 sided, 21mm. 6.8g

A modified version of the intended Edward VIII reverse was used for the brass threepences of George VI. At first they were issued simultaneously with the small silver type threepence. Within a few years the silver type was phased out and the twelve sided (dodecagonal) thick brass threepence was struck until 1967 (and in 1970 for the proof set). Early on, the Royal Mint found that the twelve sided collar placed around each coin before striking was prone to weaknesses, especially in the twelve sharp corners. During WWII the quantity of steel available for making these collars declined so in order to make the collars last longer, they were re-made with blunter corners. This experimentation led to a couple of the dates being struck with either sharp or rounded corners. See box below for more details.

Date	Peck	Mintage	Fine	VF	EF	UNC/BU
1937*	2370	45,707,957			£1	£5/£10
1937	2371	26,402 Proofs			£3	£12/£15
1938	2372	14,532,332			£5	£25/£28
1939	2374	5,603,021			£4	£30/£45
1940	2376	12,636,018			£4	£20/£25
1941**	2378/2379A	60,239,489			£2	£9/£10
1942	2380	103,214,400			£2	£9/£10
1943	2382	101,702,400			£2	£9/£10
1944	2384	69,760,000			£2	£10/£12
1945	2386	33,942,466			£3	£14/£20
1946	2388	620,734	£10	£50	£200	£650/
1948**	2390/1	4,230,400			£14	£35/£50
1949	2392	464,000		£6	£50	£150	£600/
1950	2394	1,600,000			£18	£60/£90
1950	2395	17,513 Proofs				£20/£40
1951	2396	1,184,000			£18	£70/£100
1951	2397	20,000 Proofs				£20/£40
1952	2398	25,494,400			£3	£12/£16

George VI Brass 1937 Threepence

*1937 - Two different spacings from rim to word THREE noted. They are not normally distinguished.

**Sharp and rounded corners: Varieties of George VI threepences exist with either sharp or rounded corners.

1937 - 1940: All Sharp
1941: Sharp or Rounded.
1942 - 1946: All Rounded
1948: Sharp or Rounded
1949: Sharp or Rounded.
1950 - 1952: All Sharp

ELIZABETH II Nickel-brass, 12 sided. Size/Weight as GVI

William Gardner designed the new portcullis reverse for the brass threepences of Elizabeth II. Mary Gillick was responsible for the young (first) Elizabeth II effigy.

Date	Peck	Mintage	UNC/BU
1953*	2489	30,618,000. Obv 1	£2/£4
1953*	2490	Inc above. Obv 2	£4/£6
1953*	2491	40,000 Proofs	£4/£6
1954	2492	41,720,000	£6/£7
1955	2494	41,075,200	£6/£7
1956	2496	36,801,600	£7/£8
1957	2498	24,294,400	£6/£7
1958	2500	20,504,000	£8/£12
1959	2501A	28,499,200	£5/£6
1960	2501C	83,078,400	£2/£4
1961	2501E	41,102,400	£2/£3
1962	2501G	51,545,600	£1/£2
1963	2501I	35,280,000	£1/£2
1964	ND**	44,867,200	£1/£2
1965	ND**	27,160,000	£1/£2
1966	ND**	53,760,000	60p/£1
1967	ND**	151,780,800	50p/£1
1970	ND**	750,476 Proofs from set	£2/£4
Undated error - double obverse			£375

Elizabeth II Brass 1960 Threepence

*1953 Threepences have 2 distinct levels of definition to the Queen's head. The poorly defined Obv 1 type is ex the 1953 specimen set. The sharper Obv 2 is the normal issue, a similar sharper die was also used for the 1953 proofs.

*1953 - Varieties exist with either the I of ELIZABETH pointing to a corner or with it pointing much further to the right.

** The Peck reference work was compiled in 1963. No coins newer than 1963 were catalogued.

Fourpences (Groats), non Maundy 'Britannia' type. For earlier groats, see the Maundy section.

WILLIAM IV Britannia on reverse .925 fine Silver, 16mm. Weight 1.9g

The William IV Britannia type groats were issued for use in British Guiana to replace the Quarter Guilder. The design and wording is the same as later British issues, and for that reason these coins are included here. Unlike the silver threepence, which is the same size, the Britannia groats have a milled edge.

Date	ESC	Mintage	Fine	VF	EF	UNC/BU
1836	1918	4,253,000	£5	£15	£30	£80/
1836	ND	Colons closer to D	£10	£40	£100	
1837	1922	962,280	£9	£20	£70	£120/

William IV 1836 Groat

VICTORIA Britannia on reverse .925 fine Silver, 16mm. Weight 1.9g

The reverse used for the Young head Victorian Britannia groats was the same as that used previously for William IV. The effigy is that designed by William Wyon.

Victoria 1848 Groat.
The Jubilee Head Groats had the same reverse, with the Jubilee Head obverse.

Date	ESC	Mintage	Fine	VF	EF	UNC/BU
1838	1930	2,150,280	£6	£12	£50	£100/
1838	1931A	2nd 8 struck over sideways 8				
			£10	£20	£60	£150/
1839	1932	1,461,240	£6	£20	£60	£100/
1840	1934	1,496,880	£6	£15	£50	£110/
1840	1934A	Zero in date rounder, like letter O				
1840	ND	O (zero) struck over rounder O. First reported 1994.				
1841	1935	344,520	£6	£15	£60	£110/
1841	ND	2nd 1 over upside-down 1	?			
1842	1936	724,680	£6	£15	£50	£110/
1842	1937A	2 struck over 1	£8	£30	£120	
1843	1938	1,817,640	£6	£12	£50	£110/
1843	1938A	4 over 5	£10	£25	£60	£150/
1843	ND	Double 4 in date	£10	£30	(reported 2005)	
1844	1939	855,360	£5	£20	£60	£120/
1845	1940	914,760	£5	£20	£50	£100/
1846	1941	1,366,200	£5	£15	£50	£100/
1847	1942	226,000 7 over 6	£15	£60	£240	
1848	1943	712,800	£5	£10	£50	£100/
1848	1944	2nd 8 over 6	£20	£50	£200	£450/
1848	1944A	2nd 8 over 7	£10	£35	£80	£200/
1849	1945	380,160	£6	£15	£50	£120/
1849	1946	9 over 8	£10	£20	£50	£120/
1851	1947	594,000	£30	£100	£300	£600/
1852	1948	31,300	£50	£200	£550	
1853	1949	11,880	£50	£150	£450	
1854	1952	1,096,613	£5	£10	£40	£100/
1854	ND	5 struck over 3	£5	£15	£50	£100/
1855	1953	646,041	£5	£10	£40	£100/

Jubilee head. Britannia on reverse .925 fine Silver, 16mm. Weight approx 1.9g

The Jubilee head 1888 issue was officially struck only for use in British Guiana. An example was not available at the time of writing to be weighed, so it is assumed that the weight of this coin is about the same as the previous young head issue.

Date	ESC	Mintage	Fine	VF	EF	UNC/BU
1888	1956		£10	£30	£50	£100/

GEORGE III .925 Fine Silver, 21.5mm. Weight 3g (average)
According to Herbert Grueber writing in 1899, seventy or eighty thousand pounds worth of the 1787 sixpence and shillings were coined, which would equate in numbers to low-millions of each of the two denominations. The edges are diagonally reeded, with a rope-like appearance. There had been no official issue of sixpences since 1758.

Date	ESC	Notes	Fine	VF	EF
1787	1626	No hearts reverse*	£10	£20	£70
1787	1629	Hearts reverse*	£10	£20	£70

George III 1787 Sixpence. Reproduced from a Victorian publication.

* Concerns the King's Hanoverian arms (left on the reverse of the coin) and the presence or absence of tiny hearts in the upper right segment of the arms. Clearly two different dies were used and both resulting coin types seem to be equally common.

GEORGE III .925 Fine Silver, 19mm. Weight 2.8g
The last coinage of George III (from 1816 - 1820) was designed by Benedetto Pistrucci.

Date	ESC	Mintage	Fine	VF	EF	UNC/BU
1816	1630	Inc with 1817	£10	£20	£50	£100/
1817	1632	10,921,680	£10	£20	£60	£100/
1818	1634	4,284,720	£10	£20	£25	£70	£120/
1819	1636	4,712,400	£10	£20	£50	£100/
1819	1636A	Very small 8	£10	£20	£75	£150/
1819	ND	Noted with full stop after III.				
1820	1638	1,448,960	£10	£20	£60	£100/
1820	1639A	Upside-down 1 in date	£40	£200	£500	

George III 1819 Sixpence

GEORGE IV Laureate first head .925 Fine Silver, 19mm. Weight 2.8g
The first George IV bust was by Benedetto Pistrucci. The reverses of the sixpences of George IV were basically smaller versions of the reverses used for the shillings. The first, used for 1821 only, featured a crowned ornate shield with a large rose under it. The second reverse, used 1824 to 1826 inclusive, featured a squarer shield with a circular garter surrounding it, and no rose beneath. The third reverse, which is only found with the second obverse (the design by William Wyon) was a complete change and features a lion standing on a large crown.

First head with first reverse type.

Date	ESC	Mintage	Fine	VF	EF	UNC/BU
1821	1654	863,280	£10	£35	£80	£150/
1821	1656	BBITANNIAR error	£75	£300	£700	

First head with second reverse type.

1824	1657	633,600	£10	£20	£150	£350/
1825	1659	483,120	£10	£20	£140	£300/
1826	1660	689,040	£30	£60	£250	£500/

George IV 1825 Sixpence
First head with second reverse

Bare second head with 3rd reverse type.

1826	1662	Included above	£12	£20	£100	£250/
1827	1664	166,320	£25	£75	£300	
1828	1665	15,840??	£20	£50	£200	£400/
1829	1666	403,920	£12	£35	£140	£350/

George IV 1826 Sixpence
Second head with third reverse

WILLIAM IV .925 Fine Silver, 19mm. Weight 2.8g
The William IV sixpences featured the familiar William Wyon bust (from a model by Sir Francis Chantrey) and a new wreath type reverse by Jean Baptiste Merlen.

Date	ESC	Mintage	Fine	VF	EF	UNC/BU
1831	1670	1,340,195	£10	£20	£100	£200/
1834*	1674	5,892,480	£15	£30	£110	£200/
1834	ND	3 in date double-struck				£300/
1835	1676	1,552,320	£15	£30	£100	£250/
1836	1678	1,987,920	£20	£50	£200	£300/
1837	1680	506,880	£20	£50	£200	£300/

William IV 1831 Sixpence

VICTORIA Young head .925 Fine Silver, 19mm. Weight 3g
The young head Victoria portrait, by William Wyon was changed slightly in 1867 and again in 1880. The reverse used was the same as that of William IV, although it was engraved by Leonard Charles Wyon, son of William. Coins dated 1864 to 1879 usually had a tiny die number on the reverse so that the mint staff could check the speed at which the dies became too worn or broken. What the die number on the coin happens to be usually has no bearing on the value of the coin, although some collectors do try to collect dates by die number.

Date	ESC	Mintage	Fine	VF	EF	UNC/BU
1838	1682	1,607,760	£12	£30	£100	£250/
1839	1684	3,310,560	£10	£25	£80	£200/
1840	1686	2,098,800	£15	£30	£120	£300/
1841	1687	1,386,000	£30	£90	£200	£400/
1842	1688	601,920	£15	£30	£100	£250/
1843	1689	3,160,080	£15	£30	£120	£300/
1844	1690	3,975,840	£10	£25	£100	£250/
1844	1690A	Date has large 44	£12	£30	£100	£250/
1845	1691	3,714,480	£12	£25	£100	£250/
1846	1692	4,268,880	£12	£25	£100	£250/
1847	ND	Extremely rare.				
1848	1693	586,080	£150			
1848	1693A	8 is altered 6	£100	£500		
1848	1693B	8 over 7	£150	£600		
1850	1695	498,960	£12	£25	£100	£250/
1850	1695A	5 struck over 3	£30	£80	£300	£400/
1851	1696	2,288,107	£12	£28	£100	£250/
1851	ND	Obv has one G with serif, one without. EF: £150				
1852	1697	904,586	£12	£30	£130	£250/
1853	ND	53 higher	(noted 2000)	£70		
1853	1698	3,837,930	£12	£30	£100	£250/
1854	1700	840,116			£300	£800
1855	1701	1,129,084	£12	£28	£100	£250/
1855	1701A	5 over 3 (or 5). Slightly rarer than above.				
1856*	1702	2,779,920	£12	£28	£100	£250/
1857*	1704	2,233,440	£12	£28	£100	£250/
1858	1706	1,932,480	£12	£30	£100	£250/
1858	ND	2nd 8 over 6 (London Coins 2007)	£300			
1859	1708	4,688,640	£12	£28	£100	£250/

Victoria Young Head 1853 Sixpence

* 1834 - Rarer variety exists with date in large numerals (ESC1674A).

* 1856 and 1857 can also be found with a longer line below the word PENCE (ESC 1703 and 1705 respectively). Both varieties are as common as the normal coins.

VICTORIA Young head .925 Fine Silver, 19mm. Weight 3g (continued)

Date	ESC	Mintage	Fine	VF	EF	UNC/BU
1859	1708A	9 struck over 8	£20	£70	£200	
1860	1709	1,100,880	£10	£20	£100	£250/
1862	1711	990,000	£50	£150		
1863	1712	491,040	£90	£150		£800/

Victoria Young Head 1885 Sixpence

All Sixpences (except where stated) now have a small die number above the date, until 1879.

*The Young head Victoria portrait; to the untrained eye looks the same. There were however, minor changes made in 1867, and then again in 1880. The lock of hair on the cheek was removed during 1880 and that accounts for the two types that year.

Date	ESC	Mintage	Fine	VF	EF	UNC/BU
1864	1713	4,253,040	£12	£25	£100	£250/
1865	1714	1,631,520	£12	£25	£100	£250/
1866	1715	5,140,080	£12	£25	£100	£250/
1866	1716	No die number	?	Extremely rare		
1867	1717	1,362,240	£12	£25	£100	£250/
1868	1719	1,069,200	£12	£20	£100	£250/
1869	1720	388,080	£20	£40	£200	£400/
1870	1721	479,613	£20	£40	£200	£400/
1871	1723	3,662,684	£12	£20	£100	£250/
1871	1724	No die number	£20	£40	£150	£250/
1872	1726	3,382,048	£10	£25	£100	£250/
1873	1727	4,594,733	£12	£25	£100	£250/
1874	1728	4,225,726	£12	£25	£100	£250/
1875	1729	3,256,545	£12	£25	£100	£250/
1876	1730	841,435	£15	£40	£200	
1877	1731	4,066,486	£10	£25	£100	£250/
1877	1732	No die number	£10	£25	£100	£250/
1878	1733	2,624,525	£10	£25	£100	£250/
1878	1734A	8 over 7	£50	£120	£500	
1878	ND	8 over 7, no die No.	?			
1878	1735	DRITANNIAR error	£200	£300	£700	
1879	1736	3,326,313	£50	£100	£250	

Die numbers discontinued.

Date	ESC	Mintage	Fine	VF	EF	UNC/BU
1879	1737	Included above	£10	£20	£100	£250/
1880	ND	Hair lock on cheek	£15	£35	£100	£250/
1880*	1737C	No lock of hair	£9	£20	£80	£150/
1881	1740	6,239,447	£7	£15	£70	£130/
1882	1743	759,809	£12	£30	£100	£250/
1883	1744	4,986,558	£7	£18	£60	£100/
1884	1745	3,422,565	£6	£18	£60	£100/
1885	1746	4,652,771	£7	£18	£60	£100/
1886	1748	2,728,249	£7	£20	£60	£100/
1887	1750	3,675,607	£5	£18	£55	£100/

Jubilee Head 1887 Sixpence.
The withdrawn type

Jubilee Head .925 Fine Silver, 19mm. Weight 3g

This first type Jubilee head sixpence was quickly withdrawn due to it being of similar design and roughly the same size as the half sovereign. At least one person was charged for gold plating a sixpence in order to pass it off as a half sovereign.

Reverse A: Gartered Shield, the withdrawn type.

The B type Sixpences (on the next page) have a wreath reverse, just like that of the previous Young head Sixpence.

Date	ESC	Mintage	Fine	VF	EF	UNC/BU
1887	1752	3,675,607	£5	£10	£15	£25/£30
1887	1752A	R of Victoria struck over 1		£100	£170/	
1887	1752B	JEB on truncation	£15	£30	£100	£175/£200
1887	1753	Proof				£150/

VICTORIA Jubilee Head, .925 Fine Silver, 19mm . Weight 3g (continued)

Date	ESC	Mintage	Fine	VF	EF	UNC/BU
Reverse B: Crowned Value in Wreath.						
1887	1754	Included with Rev A	£5	£8	£15	£30/
1888	1756	4,197,698	£5	£8	£25	£70/
1889	1757	8,738,928	£5	£10	£25	£75/
1890	1758	9,386,955	£6	£15	£40	£80/
1891	1759	7,022,734	£6	£15	£40	£100/
1892	1760	6,245,746	£8	£15	£40	£100/
1893*	1761	7,350,619	£300	£800	£2k	

Victoria Veiled Head 1893 Sixpence obverse.
Reverse type as Edward VII sixpence.

VICTORIA Old or Widow Head, .925 Fine Silver, 19mm. Weight 3g
Portrait by Thomas Brock, engraved by George William de Saulles. The reverse was a slightly modified version of the original Jean Baptiste Merlen design.

Date	ESC	Mintage	Fine	VF	EF	UNC/BU
1893	1762	Included above	£5	£8	£20	£75/
1894	1764	3,467,704	£6	£10	£30	£100/
1895	1765	7,024,631	£5	£10	£30	£90/
1896	1766	6,651,699	£5	£10	£30	£90/
1897	1767	5,031,498	£5	£10	£30	£90/
1898	1768	5,914,100	£5	£10	£30	£90/
1899	1769	7,996,804	£5	£10	£30	£90/
1900	1770	8,984,354	£8	£10	£35	£90/
1901	1771	5,108,757	£5	£9	£30	£80/

EDWARD VII .925 Fine Silver, 19mm. Weight 3g
From this reign onwards the use of a reducing machine was adopted. The artist is responsible for creating a large version of the design and the old job of creating a smaller version to strike coins is now undertaken mechanically, the engraver being made quite redundant in this respect! George William de Saulles was responsible for the Edward VII portrait and the reverse was a modified version of the previous old head Victoria type.

Date	ESC	Mintage	Fine	VF	EF	UNC/BU
1902	1785	6,367,378	£5	£10	£30	£70/
1902	1786	15,123 Proofs with matte finish				£80/
1903	1787	5,410,096	£6	£15	£50	£100/
1904	1788	4,487,098	£6	£20	£90	£200/
1905	1789	4,235,556	£6	£20	£80	£200/
1906	1790	7,641,146	£6	£15	£40	£100/
1907	1791	8,733,673	£6	£15	£50	£100/
1908	1792	6,739,491	£6	£15	£50	£100/
1909	1793	6,584,017	£6	£15	£50	£100/
1910	1794	12,490,724	£5	£9	£35	£75/

Edward VII 1906 Sixpence

GEORGE V .925 Fine Silver (until 1920) 19mm. Weight 3g
The bust was by Bertram MacKennal, the reverse was a smaller version of that used for the shilling, which was essentially a modified version of that used for the Edward VII shilling and designed originally by de Saulles.

Date	ESC	Mintage	Fine	VF	EF	UNC/BU
1911	1795	9,155,310	BV	£5	£20	£40/£50
1911	1796	6,007 Proofs				£75/
1912	1797	10,984,129	BV	£6	£25	£60/
1913	1798	7,499,833	BV	£9	£32	£65/
1914	1799	22,714,602	BV	£5	£15	£40/£50
1915	1800	15,694,597	BV	£5	£15	£45/£55
1916	1801	22,207,178	BV	£5	£15	£40/
1917	1802	7,725,475	£3	£12	£35	£100/
1918	1803	27,558,743	BV	£5	£15	£40/£50
1919	1804	13,375,447	BV	£4	£18	£45/£55
1920	1805	14,136,287. Ag .925	£3	£8	£25	£60/£70

George V 1926 Sixpence. 1st reverse type.
Early (1st Effigy) sixpences have a slightly larger bust.

GEORGE V Now debased to .500 Silver, 19mm. Weight 2.88g

Date	ESC	Mintage	Fine	VF	EF	UNC/BU
1920	1806		£2	£4	£25	£50/
1921	1807	30,339,741	£2	£4	£15	£60/
1922	1808	16,878,890	£2	£4	£20	£60/
1923	1809	6,382,793	£2	£4	£20	£50/
1924	1810	17,444,218	£2	£4	£20	£45/
1925	1811	12,720,558	£2	£5	£16	£40/
1925	1812	With new broader rim	£2	£4	£14	£40/
1926	1813	21,809,261	£2	£5	£18	£40/
1926	1814	Modified Effigy (Ap 1)	£2	£5	£12	£35/
1927	1815	68,939,873	£2	£4	£12	£35/
1927	1816	15,000 Proofs.New Oak/Acorn reverse				£40/£50
1928	1817	23,123,384	BV	£2	£10	£25/
1929	1818	28,319,326	BV	£2	£10	£25/£35
1930	1819	16,990,289	BV	£2	£15	£25/£35
1931**	1820	16,873,268	£2	£5	£20	£30/£40
1932	1821	9,406,117	£2	£4	£12	£35/£45
1933	1822	22,185,083	£2	£5	£9	£30/£40
1934	1823	9,304,009	£2	£5	£10	£30/£40
1935	1824	13,995,621	BV	BV	£6	£25/£35
1936	1825	24,380,171	BV	BV	£5	£25/£35

George V 1934 Sixpence.
2nd reverse type

** George V Sixpences from 1931 onwards have finer edge millings.

EDWARD VIII .500 Silver 19mm
The reverse, featuring six linked rings of St. Edmund was designed by George Kruger Gray. The obverse was by Thomas Humphrey Paget. Like all Edward VIII coins, this was not officially issued.

Date	ESC	Mintage	Fine	VF	EF	UNC/BU
1937	1825B	3 or 4 known	Very expensive			

GEORGE VI .500 Silver (until 1946) 19mm. Weight 2.8g
The obverse portrait of all George VI coins was by Thomas Humphrey Paget. The reverse is by George Kruger Gray.
From 1947 the silver content was completely removed and the new coins were made from a copper and nickel alloy
(Cupro-Nickel). In 1949 the King gave up his IND:IMP (Emperor of India) title due to that countries new independence. Partly in order to fill the space this left, the 1949 reverse was redesigned to use a different monogram.

Date	ESC	Mintage	EF	UNC/BU
1937	1826	22,302,524	BV	£7/£8
1937	1827	26,402 Proofs		£10/£15
1938	1828	13,402,701	BV	£18/£30
1939	1829	28,670,304	BV	£10/£15
1940	1830	20,875,196	BV	£10/£15
1941	1831	23,186,616	BV	£10/£15
1942	1832	44,942,785	BV	£10/£15
1943	1833	46,927,111	BV	£8/£15
1944	1834	37,952,600	BV	£8/£15
1945	1835	39,939,259	BV	£8/£14
1946	1836	43,466,407	BV	£8/£14

George VI 1939 Sixpence.
1st reverse

GEORGE VI Cupro-Nickel (No silver), 19mm. Weight 2.8g
(weights seem to be slightly more for the new monogram type, 1949 - 1952)

Date	ESC	Mintage	EF	UNC/BU
1947	1837	29,993,263	£1	£6/£7
1948	1838	88,323,540	£1	£6/£7
1949*	1838A	41,355,515	£1	£8/£10
1950	1838B	32,741,955	£1	£9/£15
1950	1838C	17,513 Proofs	£1	£10/£15
1951	1838D	40,399,491	£1	£7/£14
1951	1838E	20,000 Proofs	£1	£10/£15
1952	1838F	1,013,477	VF:£15 £40	£80/£150

George VI Sixpence
2nd reverse used from 1949 - 52.

ELIZABETH II Cupro-Nickel (No silver), 19mm . Weight 2.8g
Portrait by Mary Gillick, reverse is by Edgar Fuller, modeled by Cecil Thomas. From 1954 the title BRITT OMN
was omitted. All ESC numbers start with 1838, followed by the letter shown.

Date	ESC	Mintage	UNC/BU
1953	H	70,323,876	£2/£3
1953	G	40,000 Proofs	£3/£5
1954*	I	105,241,150	£4/£5
1955	J	109,929,554	£6/£7
1956	K	109,841,555	£4/£5
1957	L	105,654,290	£3/£4
1958	M	123,518,527	£5/£6
1959	N	93,089,441	£1/£2
1960	O	103,288,346	£5/£6
1961	P	115,052,017	£5/£6
1962	Q	178,359,637	£2/£3
1963	R	112,964,000	£3/£4
1964	S	152,336,000	£1/£2
1965	T	129,644,000	£1/£2
1966	U	175,696,000	50p/£1
1967	V	240,788,000	30p/£1
1970	W	750,476 Proofs	£3/£4

Elizabeth II 1955 Sixpence

The shilling of 1763 is known as the 'Northumberland' shilling, as it was made to be first distrubuted by the Earl of Northumberland upon becoming Lord Lieutenant of Ireland. Old literature states that £100 worth was coined, which would equate to only 2000 coins. An unknown quality must have been subsequently produced - the coin is quite scarce but the numbers of known coins would suggest that more than 2000 were made. The 1787 issue of shillings is very similar to that of the 1787 sixpence - see sixpence section.

GEORGE III .925 Fine Silver, 25.2mm. Weight 6g (average)

Date	ESC	Notes	Fine	VF	EF
1763	1214	'Northumberland'	£300	£600	£1000
1787	1216	No hearts reverse*	£12	£30	£80
1787	1218	NH, no stop over head	£25	£60	£150
1787	ND	NH, 1 over mirrored 1	Exists?		
1787	1222	NH, no stop at date	£20	£50	£140
1787	1223	NH, no obverse stops	£200	£700	£2000
1787	1225	With hearts reverse*	£12	£30	£80
1787	1225A	WH, 1 over mirrored 1	£50	£100	£350

* Concerns the King's Hanoverian arms (reverse arms at 9 o'clock) and the presence or absence of tiny hearts in the upper right segment of the arms (NH = No hearts, WH = With hearts). Clearly different dies were used and both resulting coin types seem equally common.

During the latter part of the 18th century captured Spanish colonial silver coins were circulating in Great Britain due to the lack of proper silver coinage. In 1797 the government made this more official by countermarking Spanish colonial coins and making them legal tender for various face values. It wasn't until 1816/17 that a proper re-coinage was undertaken at the new Royal Mint building at Tower Hill, which was fully equipped with the new and proven Boulton/Watt technology (see notes for Cartwheel Twopence). One of the first coins to be struck was the shilling, which interestingly, remained legal tender as 1/20th of a pound sterling until the decimal equivalent (the 5p) was made smaller in 1990. The portrait of George III was the work of Benedetto Pistrucci, as was the reverse. The dies were cut by Thomas Wyon.

George III 1763 Northumberland Shilling. Reproduced from a Victorian publication.

GEORGE III .925 Fine Silver, 23.5mm. Weight 5.65g

Date	ESC	Mintage	Fine	VF	EF	UNC/BU
1816	1228		£8	£20	£80	£150/
1817	1232	23,031,360	£8	£20	£90	£150/
1817	1232A	R over E - GEOE			£500	
1817	ND	RRIT Error		£70	£200	
1818	1234	1,342,440	£10	£35	£120	£300/
1818	1234A	2nd 8 higher	£30	£60	£200	
1819	1235	7,595,280	£10	£20	£100	£180/
1819	ND	9 over 6			£250	
1819	1235A	9 over 8	£20	£50	£150	£300/
1820	1236	7,975,440	£15	£30	£100	£180/
1820	1236A	1 of HONI over S	£100			
1820	ND	H of HONI over sideways H		?		

George III 1787 Shilling

George III 1816 Shilling

The first George IV bust was by Benedetto Pistrucci. The obverses and reverses used were the same as the sixpences. The first - used for 1821 only - featured a crowned ornate shield with a large rose under it. The second reverse, used 1823 to 1825, featured a squarer shield with a circular garter surrounding it, and no rose beneath. The third reverse, which is only found with the second obverse (the design by William Wyon) was a complete change and features a lion standing on a large crown.

The first Laureate Head of George IV, shown with the first and second reverse types.

GEORGE IV .925 Fine silver, around 23.5mm. Weight 5.65g

Date	ESC	Mintage	Fine	VF	EF	UNC/BU
1st Head - Laureate Roman style, 1st shield reverse.						
1821	1247	2,463,120		£15	£50	£175 £400/
1st Head - Laureate Roman style, 2nd shield reverse.						
1823	1249	693,000	£100	£200	£300	£700/
1824	1251	4,158,000	£15	£50	£150	£500/
1825	1253	2,459,160	£15	£50	£200	£450/
1825	1253B	5 struck over 3	?			
2nd head - Bare type, 3rd reverse with large lion and crown.						
1825	1254	Inc above	£15	£40	£120	£300/
1825	1254A	Roman 1 for 1 in date.	£100			
1826	1257	6,351,840	£15	£30	£100	£250/
1826	1257A	6 over 2	?			
1827	1259	574,200	£40	£120	£400	£900/
1829	1260	879,120	£30	£70	£250	£500/

The second (bare) head and its only reverse (the third George IV shilling reverse)

WILLIAM IV .925 Fine silver, just over 23mm. Weight 5.65g
A larger version of the sixpence, the William IV shilling featured the familiar William Wyon bust (from a model by Sir Francis Chantrey) and wreath type reverse by Jean Baptiste Merlen.

Date	ESC	Mintage	Fine	VF	EF	UNC/BU
1834	1268	3,223,440	£18	£40	£180	£350/
1835	1271	1,449,360	£20	£45	£200	£500/
1836	1273	3,567,960	£20	£45	£200	£400/
1837	1276	479,160	£40	£100	£400	
1837	ND	R over low A	?			

William IV Shilling obverse. The reverse used was the wreath type, as with Young Head Victorian Shillings.

VICTORIA .925 Fine silver, around 23.5mm. Weight 5.65g
The Young Head design was the work of William Wyon, the reverse used was basically that used previously for William IV. A few minor changes were made to the bust to age it, although it looked very similar even 50 years into the reign, when it was replaced by the Jubilee bust. Small die numbers were used on the reverse of the dates indicated.

Victoria Young head 1839 Shilling

Date	ESC	Mintage	Fine	VF	EF	UNC/BU
1st Young Head (with W.W.)						
1838	1278	1,956,240	£20	£40	£150	£400/
1839	1280	5,666,760	£30	£90	£250	£500/
2nd Young Head (with minor changes).						
1839	1283	No W.W. at neck	£20	£40	£150	£350/
1839	ND	2nd A in BRIT... unbarred (2013 London Coins) £750 UNC				
1840	1285	1,639,440	£25	£50	£200	£400/
1841	1287	875,160	£30	£80	£300	
1842	1288	2,094,840	£20	£35	£200	£400/
1843	1290	1,465,200	£50	£100	£300	£900/
1844	1291	4,466,880	£20	£35	£120	£400/
1845	1292	4,082,760	£20	£45	£150	£400/
1846	1293	4,031,280	£20	£35	£150	£400/
1848	ND	1,041,480 (More common with 8/6)		£700 EF approx.		
1848	1294	2nd 8 over 6	£100	£220		
1849	1295	645,480	£20	£40	£160	£400/
1850	1296	685,080	£500	£1400		
1850	1297	50 over 49 (or 46)	£700		£4000	
1851	1298	470,071	£100	£250	£700	£1300/
1852	1299	1,306,574	£15	£35	£120	£300/
1853	1300	4,256,188	£15	£35	£120	£300/
1854	1302	552,414	£200	£400		
1854	1302A	4 over 1	£400			
1855	1303	1,368,499	£15	£30	£120	£300/
1856	1304	3,168,000	£12	£25	£120	£250/
1857	1305	2,562,120	£14	£30	£150	£300/
1857	1305A	Inverted G for D in FD	?			
1858	1306	3,108,600	£14	£30	£150	£300/
1858	ND	8 over 8		NEF	£300? Approx	
1859	1307	4,561,920	£14	£30	£140	£300/
1859	ND	9 over 8 (or ??) NF: £95 (R Ingram 2006)				
1860	1308	1,671,120	£15	£40	£150	£300/
1860	ND	8 over 8			£300	£600/£700
1861	1309	1,382,040	£15	£40	£150	£150/
1861	1309A	D over B in F:D:	GVF: £650 (2013)			
1861	ND	1 over tilted 1 Approx			£300	£500/
1862	1310	954,360	£50	£120	£350	£650/
1863	1311	859,320	£150	£300		
1863	1311A	3 over 1		£400		
All shillings (except where stated) now have a small die number above the date until 1879.						
1864	1312	4,518,360	£15	£30	£150	£250/
1865	1313	5,619,240	£15	£30	£100	£220/
1866	1314	4,989,600	£15	£30	£100	£220/
1866	1314A	BBITANNIAR error		£400		
1867	1315	2,166,120	£15	£30	£100	£250/

VICTORIA .925 Fine silver, around 23.5mm. Weight 5.65g (continued)

3rd Young Head (with minor changes).

Date	ESC	Mintage	Fine	VF	EF	UNC/BU
1867*	1316		£200			
1868	1318	3,330,360	£12	£30	£100	£250/
1869	1319	736,560	£15	£30	£180	£300/
1870	1320	1,467,471	£15	£30	£120	£300/
1871	1321	4,910,010	£15	£30	£100	£350/
1872	1324	8,897,781	£15	£30	£100	£250/
1872	ND	Raised dot between R and A in GRATIA. NVF: £100+				
1873	1325	6,489,598	£10	£25	£100	£250/
1874	1326	5,503,747	£10	£25	£100	£250/
1874	ND	With crosslet 4	?			
1875	1327	4,353,983	£10	£30	£100	£250/
1876	1328	1,057,487	£15	£40	£120	£250/
1877*	1329	2,980,703	£10	£25	£100	£200/
1878	1330	3,127,131	£10	£40	£100	£200/
1878		As above with die number 1				£1000/
1878	ND	Last R in BRITANNIAR over A. Reported 2006.				
1879	1332	3,611,507	£200			

4th Young Head (slightly older features and other minor differences).

Date	ESC	Mintage	Fine	VF	EF	UNC/BU
1879	1334	No die no.	£10	£20	£100	£250/
1880	1335	4,842,786	£10	£20	£100	£250/
1881*	1338	5,255,332	£10	£22	£100	£250/
1882	1341	1,611,786	£20	£50	£150	£250/
1883	1342	7,281,4.50	£10	£20	£80	£150/
1884	1343	3,923,993	£10	£20	£80	£150/
1885	1345	3,336,527	£5	£10	£80	£150/
1886	1347	2,086,819	£5	£10	£80	£150/
1887	1349	4,034,133 Young Head	£15	£30	£120	£250/

* 1867 with the third lower relief Young head has not been confirmed to exist. 1877 is also believed to exist without a die number. A variety of 1881 exists with a shorter line under the word SHILLING (ESC 1338A). Both varieties are thought to be equally common.

Victoria Jubilee head 1887 Shilling

VICTORIA Jubilee Head type .925 Fine silver, around 23.5mm . Weight 5.65g
Sir Joseph Boehm designed the Jubilee head, which was engraved by Leonard Charles Wyon. Mr Wyon also engraved the reverse, but from his own design. In 1889 the head was made slightly larger. The old head bust was by Sir Thomas Brock, the reverse of the old head shilling was by Sir Edward Poynter. Both sides were engraved by G W de Saulles.

Date	ESC	Mintage	Fine	VF	EF	UNC/BU
1887*	1351	Included above	£3	£10	£20	£30/
1887	1352	1,312 Proofs				£250/
1888	1353	4,526,856 Last 8/7	£8	£10	£40	£100/
1889	1354	7,039,628 small head				£500
1889	1355	Larger head	£8	£11	£40	£100/
1890	1357	8,794,042	£8	£11	£50	£100/
1891	1358	5,565,348	£10	£15	£50	£120/
1892	1360	4,591,622	£10	£15	£50	£120/

1887 - Varieties with the device that divides the '18' and '87'.

The device pointing to a rim tooth is scarcer than when the device points between two rim teeth.

Old, Veiled or Widow Head type. Weight 5.65g:

Date	ESC	Mintage	Fine	VF	EF	UNC/BU
1893	1361	7,039,074	£6	£12	£30	£100/
1893	1361A	Small letters Obv	£6	£15	£35	£100/
1893	1362	1,312 Proofs				£250/
1894	1363	5,953,152	£10	£18	£40	£100/
1895	1364	8,880,651 Small rose *	£10	£20	£45	£100/
1895	1364A	Larger rose on Rev*	£6	£15	£35	£90/
1896	1365	9,264,551 Large rose *	£6	£15	£35	£100/
1896	1365A	Smaller rose on Rev*	£10	£25	£50	£130/
1897	1366	6,270,364	£6	£15	£35	£90/£120
1898	1367	9,768,703	£6	£15	£35	£90/£120
1899	1368	10,965,382	£6	£15	£40	£90/£120
1900	1369	10,937,590	£6	£15	£35	£80/£100
1901	1370	3,426,294	£6	£15	£35	£80/£100

*See next page

Victoria Veiled head 1895 Shilling

Victoria 1895 Shilling detail, showing large rose type
(left) and small rose type (right)

EDWARD VII .925 Fine silver, 23.6mm. Weight 5.65g
Both the obverse and reverse were designed and engraved by George William de Saulles.

Date	ESC	Mintage	Fine	VF	EF	UNC/BU
1902	1410	7,809,481	£6	£10	£40	£65/£75
1902	1411	15,123 Proofs with matte finish				£80/£100
1903	1412	2,061,823	£8	£20	£150	£350/
1904	1413	2,040,161	£10	£25	£120	£300/
1905	1414	488,390	£100	£450	£1500	
1906	1415	10,791,025	£6	£15	£70	£150/
1907	1416	4,083,418	£8	£20	£75	£200/
1908	1417	3,806,969	£10	£30	£150	£450/
1909	1418	5,664,982	£10	£30	£150	£450/
1910	1419	26,547,236	£6	£8	£40	£100/

Forgeries exist of 1905 shillings.

GEORGE V .925 Fine silver (until 1920), 23.6mm. Weight 5.65g
Bust by Sir Bertram MacKennal, reverse as Edward VII type.

Edward VII 1910 Shilling

Date	ESC	Mintage	Fine	VF	EF	UNC/BU
1911*	1420	20,065,901	BV	£6	£25	£70/£80
1911	1421	6,007 Proofs				£80/£90
1912**	1422	15,594,009	BV	£14	£35	£80/
1913	1423	9,011,509	£6	£15	£50	£150/
1914	1424	23,415,843	BV	£5	£25	£50/
1915	1425	39,279,024	BV	£4	£20	£50/
1916	1426	35,862,015	BV	£4	£20	£50/
1917	1427	22,202,608	BV	£5	£30	£60/
1918	1428	34,915,934	BV	£5	£25	£50/
1919	1429	10,823,824	£6	£9	£30	£70/

Reduced to .500 silver. Size and weight as above.

1920	1430	22,825,142	£3	£10	£30	£75/
1921		22,648,763				
	ND	earlier, deeper cut bust	£15	£40	£150	
1921	1431	later, shallow larger bust	£3	£15	£35	£80/£100
1922	1432	27,215,738	£3	£4	£25	£70/
1923	1433	14,575,243	£3	£4	£25	£70/
1924	1434	9,250,095	£3	£6	£30	£60/
1925	1435	5,418,764	£6	£20	£60	£120/
1926	1436	22,516,453	£3	£5	£20	£60/
1926	1437	Mod Effigy (see Appendix I) £3	£3	£5	£15	£40/
1927	1438	9,262,344	£3	£5	£20	£45/

George V 1915 1st type Shilling, 1911-26. The
reverse is almost identical to the Edward
VII reverse.

1911 exists with the following 3 obverse types:
Obv 1: 'I' of GEORGIUS to space.
Obv 2: 'I' of GEORGIUS to bead and
shallow neck.
Obv 3: 'I' of GEORGIUS to bead and fuller
neck.

**1912 has been reported with the 'IMP'
closely spaced and widely spaced: 'I M P'.

GEORGE V .925 Fine silver (until 1920), 23.6mm. Weight 5.65g
A new design with no inner circle and the date to the right. Obverse by MacKennel, reverse by George Kruger Gray.

Date	ESC	Mintage	Fine	VF	EF	UNC/BU
1927	1439	New design		£3	£12	£35/
1927	1440	15,000 Proofs				£50/£60
1928	1441	18,136,778		BV	£5	£25/£30
1929	1442	19,343,006		BV	£5	£25/£30
1930	1443	3,137,092	£6	£20	£40	£100/
1931	1444	6,993,926		BV	£6	£25/£35
1932	1445	12,168,101		BV	£10	£25/£35
1933	1446	11,511,624		BV	£6	£20/£30
1934	1447	6,138,463		£5	£12	£30/£40
1935	1448	9,183,462		BV	£10	£20/£25
1936	1449	11,910,613		BV	£10	£20/£25

EDWARD VIII, .500 silver, just over 23mm
The reverse was the George VI Scottish type designed by George Kruger Gray.
The obverse was by Thomas Humphrey Paget. Like all Edward VIII coins, this was
not officially issued.

Date	ESC	Mintage	Fine	VF	EF	UNC/BU
1936	1449B	Pattern Scottish type only			Extremely Rare	

George V 1929 2nd type Shilling. 1927-36

GEORGE VI .500 silver (until 1947), just over 23mm. Weight 5.6lg
The reverses were by George Kruger Gray. The obverse was by Thomas Humphrey Paget.

Date	ESC	Mintage	EF	UNC/BU
1937E	1450	8,359,122		£9/£12
1937E	1451	Proof 26,402		£10/£25
1937S	1452	6,748,875		£7/£10
1937S	1453	Proof 26,402		£8/£15
1938E	1454	4,833,436		£30/£40
1938S	1455	4,797,852		£25/£30
1939E	1456	11,052,677		£10/£15
1939S	1457	10,263,892		£10/£15
1940E	1458	11,099,126		£10/£15
1940S	1459	9,913,089		£9/£12
1941E	1460	11,391,883		£10/£15
1941S	1461	8,086,030		£8/£10
1942E	1462	17,453,643		£10/£15
1942S	1463	13,676,759		£8/£10
1943E	1464	11,404,213		£7/£10
1943S	1465	9,824,214		£7/£10
1944E	1466	11,586,752		£7/£10
1944S	1467	10,990,167		£7/£10
1945E	1468	15,143,404		£7/£8
1945S	1469	15,106,270		£7/£8
1946E	1470	18,663,797 **		£6/£7
1946S	1471	16,381,501		£6/£7

George VI 1942 English type Shilling

From 1937 - 1966 (and again for the 1970 proofs) Shillings were struck with either an English or Scottish reverse type. They circulated, generally, throughout the United Kingdom and are indicated in this book by the suffix E or S after the date.

Cupro-Nickel (no silver content) Type as before. Weight 5.68g

Date	ESC	Mintage	EF	UNC/BU
1947E	1472	12,120,611		£7/£8
1947S	1473	12,282,223		£7/£8
1948E	1474	45,576,923		£7/£8
1948S	1475	45,351,937		£7/£8

IND : IMP in legend discontinued.

Date	ESC	Mintage	EF	UNC/BU
1949E	1475A	19,328,405	£2	£15/£20
1949S	1475B	21,243,074	£2	£15/£20
1950E	1475C	19,243,872	£5	£15/£20
1950E	1475D	17,513 Proofs	FDC	£20
1950S	1475E	14,299,601	£5	£15/£20
1950S	1475F	17,513 Proofs	FDC	£20
1951E	1475G	9,956,930	£3	£15/£20
1951E	1475H	20,000 Proofs	FDC	£20
1951S	1475I	10,961,174	£3	£15/£20
1951S	1475J	20,000 Proofs	FDC	£20
1952E	1475*	1 known outside of the Royal Collection.		

George VI Scottish type Shilling reverse

** 1946E has been reported with two reverse varieties concerning the pointing of the 'IND'.
Reverse A: The 'I' points to a rim bead. Reverse B: The 'I' points between two beads.

As with a lot of minor varieties on common coins, this is rarely distinguished and the values are assumed to be the same.

ELIZABETH II, Cupro-Nickel (no silver), 23.6mm. Weight 5.63g
The young Elizabeth portrait was designed by Mary Gillick. The English and Scottish reverse types were by William Gardner. As with all the Elizabeth II coins, the BRITT OMN was removed in 1954. All the shillings below have the ESC number 1475 followed by the letter(s) shown.

Date	ESC	Mintage	EF	UNC/BU
1953E	K	41,942,894		£2/£4
1953	ND	Head both sides.		£300/
		Undated but BRITT:OMN present		
1953E	L	Proofs 40,000	FDC	£10
1953S	M	20,663,528		£5/£7
1953S	N	40,000 Proofs	FDC	£8
1954E	O	30,262,032		£5/£7
1954S	P	26,771,735		£7/£9
1955E	Q	45,259,908		£9/£12
1955S	R	27,950,906		£8/£10
		Also exists with broader rim.		
1956E	S	44,907,008		£11/£15
1956S	T	42,853,637		£10/£14
1957E	U	42,774,217		£8/£10
1957S	V	17,959,988		£15/£18
1958E	W	14,392,305		£20/£30
1958S	X	40,822,557		£3/£4
1959E	Y	19,442,778		£4/£8
1959S	Z	1,012,988	£4	£30/£50
1960E	AA	27,027,914		£5/£7
1960S	BB	14,376,932		£5/£7
1961E	CC	39,816,907		£4/£6
1961S	DD	2,762,558	£2	£10/£20
1962E	EE	36,704,379		£4/£6
1962S	FF	18,967,310		£4/£6
1963E	GG	44,714,000		£2/£3
1963S	HH	32,300,000		£2/£3
1964E	II	8,590,900		£2/£3
1964S	JJ	5,239,100		£2/£5
1965E	KK	9,218,000		£1/£2
1965S	LL	2,774,000		£1/£2
1966E	MM	15,005,000 *		£1/£2
1966S	NN	15,607,000 *		£1/£2
1966S		Wrong alignment **		£100/
1970E	OO	Proofs 750,476 from set		£4/
1970S	PP	Proofs 750,476 from set		£4/

Elizabeth II 1965 Scottish type Shilling

The Elizabeth II English type reverse

* Mintage number includes some struck in 1967, but dated 1966.
** Coin struck with incorrect 'Coin' alignment, see appendix I.

Eighteenpence Bank tokens (One Shilling and Sixpence)

This interesting series, issued under the authority of the Bank of England was an authorised token issue providing much needed change until the major re-coinage of 1816. Two bust types were used on them during their short date run. The first bust was the military type as illustrated on the THREE SHILLING page. The second bust was a not all-that attractive laureate head type, shown below.

GEORGE III .925 Fine Silver, 26mm. Weight, about 7.3g

Date	ESC	Details	F	VF	EF	UNC/BU
1811	969	(1st head)	£15	£30	£75	£200/
1812	971	(1st head)	£15	£25	£60	£150/
1812	972	(2nd head from here)	£14	£28	£80	£200/
1813	976		£14	£28	£80	£180/
1814	977		£14	£28	£80	£180/
1815	978		£14	£28	£80	£180/
1816	979		£14	£28	£80	£180/

Florins / Two Shillings

Second head Eighteenpence Bank Token of 1814

VICTORIA .925 fine silver, 28mm. Weight 11.31g. The Godless Florin.
During a time when christianity was more widely practiced and being a good christian was a focal point of most peoples lives, it was probably asking for trouble to produce a coin for circulation omitting the words 'DEI GRATIA' (For the grace of God). Even though it was pretty revolutionary, being one tenth of a pound, and therefore Britain's first decimal coin, it didn't last long, and was replaced two years later by a redesigned 'Gothic' style florin. William Wyon designed both obverses and William Dyce was responsible for both reverses. Confusingly for novices, the Gothic florins have no numerical date on them, instead, it is in Roman Numerals at the end of the obverse legend.

Date	ESC	Mintage	Latin Date	Fine	VF	EF	UNC/BU
1849	802	413,830		£20	£45	£160	£300/
1849	802A	'WW' initials partly obliterated		£50	£200	£400/	

VICTORIA .925 fine silver, 30mm. Weight approx 11.35g. The Gothic Florin.

Date	ESC	Mintage	Latin Date	Fine	VF	EF	UNC/BU
1851	803	1,540	mdcccli	Proof, very rare			
1852	806	1,014,552	mdccclii	£20	£60	£200	£400/
1852	807A	ii struck over i				£300	£600/
1853	807B	3,919,950	mdcccliii	£15	£60	£200	£400/
1853	808	With no stop after date.		£20	£60	£250	£500/
1854	811	550,413	mdcccliv	£700			
1855	812	831,017	mdccclv	£40	£100		
1856	813	2,201,760	mdccclvi	£15	£50	£200	£500/
1856	813A	With no stop after date.		£30	£100	£400	
1857	814	1,671,120	mdccclvii	£15	£50	£250	£500/
1858	816	2,239,380	mdccclviii	£20	£60	£300	£600/
1858	816B	With no stop after date.		£20	£50	£250	£500/
1859	817	2,568,060	mdccclvix	£22	£70	£300	£500/
1859	818	With no stop after date.	Rare				

Victoria 1849 'Godless' Florin

VICTORIA .925 fine silver, 30mm. Weight approx 11.35g. The Gothic Florin

Date	ESC	Mintage	Latin Date	Fine	VF	EF	UNC/BU
1860	819	1,475,100	mdccclx	£18	£70	£300	£500/
1862	820	594,000	mdccclxii		£300	£1500	
1863	822	938,520	mdccclxiii		£1200		
1864	824	1,861,200	mdccclxiv	£20	£75	£300	£600/
1865	826	1,580,044	mdccclxv	£25	£100	£350	£700/
1866	828	914,760	mdccclxvi	£25	£85	£300	
	829	With colon after date.		Rare			
1867	830	423,720	mdccclxvii	£20	£70	£250	£500/
1867	832A	No 'WW' (42 arcs in border)		Extremely rare			
1868	833	896,940	mdccclxviii	£40	£80	£350	
1869	834	297,000	mdccclxix	£45	£100	£300	
1870	836	1,080,648	mdccclxx	£35	£80	£250	£500/
1871	837	3,425,605	mdccclxxi	£25	£55	£250	£500/
1872	840	7,199,690	mdccclxxii	£20	£45	£200	£450/
1873	841	5,921,839	mdccclxxiii	£20	£45	£250	£500/
1874	843	1,642,630	mdccclxxiv	£20	£60	£250	£400/
1874	843A	iv struck over iii		£160			
1875	844	1,117,030	mdccclxxv	£20	£50	£200	£500/
1876	845	580,034	mdccclxxvi	£30	£80	£250	
1877	846	682,292	mdccclxxvii	£25	£80	£250	£500/
	847	No 'WW' (48 arcs in border)			£500		
	848	No 'WW' (42 arcs in border)			£400		
1878	849	1,786,680	mdccclxxviii	£20	£50	£250	£400/
1879	1,512,247		mdccclxxix :				
	849B	Die No. present, 48 arcs	?	(with WW)	?		
	850	42 border arcs		£100	(no WW initials)		
	851	No Die No. 48 border arcs	£20	£50	£250	£500/	
	852	38 border arcs		£30	£60	£250	
1880	854A	Portrait as 1868-1877. It's difficult to describe the difference between this and the normal 1880 coin below. This type is extremely rare.					
1880	854	2,167,170	mdccclxxx	£20	£50	£200	£400/
1881	856	2,570,337	mdccclxxxi	£20	£50	£200	£400/
	858A	Broken die, last 'x' looks like an 'r'			£300	£500/	
1883	859	3,555,667	mdccclxxxiii	£15	£50	£200	£400/
1884	860	1,447,379	mdccclxxxiv	£15	£50	£200	£400/
1885	861	1,758,210	mdccclxxxv	£18	£50	£200	£400/
1886	863	591,773	mdccclxxxvi	£15	£45	£200	£350/
1887	865	1,776,903	mdccclxxxvii	?			
1887	866	'WW' present (46 arcs in border)		£70	£300	£550/	

Victoria 1864 'Gothic' Florin

VICTORIA .925 fine silver, Jubilee Head type 29.5mm. Weight approx 11.3g.
Sir Joseph Boehm designed the Jubilee head, which was engraved by Leonard Charles Wyon. Mr Wyon also engraved the reverse, but from his own design. The old head bust was by Sir Thomas Brock, the reverse of the old head florin was by Sir Edward Poynter. Both sides of the old head florin were engraved by George William de Saulles.

Date	ESC	Mintage	Fine	VF	EF	UNC/BU
1887	868	Incl. with Gothic	£10	£16	£25	£50/£70
1887	869	1,084 Jubilee Head Proofs			£50	£300/£400
1888	870	1,541,540	£10	£20	£60	£150/
1889	871	2,973,561	£10	£20	£75	£150/
1890	872	1,684,737	£15	£40	£150	£400/£500
1891	873	836,438	£30	£100	£350	
1892	874	283,401	£50	£150	£350	

VICTORIA .925 fine silver, Veiled or Widow Head 28.5mm. Weight approx 11.3g.

Date	ESC	Mintage	Fine	VF	EF	UNC/BU
1893	876	1,666,103	£9	£20	£50	£100/£130
1894	878	1,952,842	£9	£30	£80	£200/£300
1895	879	2,182,968	£9	£20	£65	£180/£250
1896	880	2,944,416	£9	£20	£65	£180/£250
1897	881	1,699,921	£9	£20	£65	£160/£200
1898	882	3,061,343	£10	£20	£65	£160/£200
1899	883	3,966,953	£10	£20	£65	£160/£200
1900	884	5,528,630	£10	£20	£65	£100/£150
1901	885	2,648,870	£10	£20	£65	£100/£150

Victoria Jubilee Head 1887 Florin

EDWARD VII .925 fine silver, 28.5mm. Weight approx 11.3g.
Both the obverse and reverse were designed and engraved by George William de Saulles.

Date	ESC	Mintage	Fine	VF	EF	UNC/BU
1902	919	2,489,575	£15	£25	£70	£90/£120
1902	920	15,123 Matt finish Proofs				£80/£150
1903	921	1,995,298	£20	£50	£150	£350/
1904	922	2,769,932	£20	£55	£170	£400/
1905	923	1,187,596	£50	£200	£900	
1906	924	6,910,128	£15	£30	£120	£350/
1907	925	5,947,895	£15	£30	£150	£350/
1908	926	3,280,010	£20	£70	£300	£900/
1909	927	3,482,289	£22	£70	£250	£550/
1910	928	5,650,713	£10	£25	£150	£250/£350

Victoria Veiled Head 1893 Florin

Edward VII 1902 Florin

GEORGE V .925 fine silver (until 1919) 28.5mm. Weight approx 11.3g.
The obverse is by Sir Bertram MacKennal (modified at various stages) and the first reverse design, based on the Jubilee Victoria issue is by an unknown designer, probably completed in house. From 1927 onwards the new reverse used was designed by George Kruger Gray.

Date	ESC	Mintage	Fine	VF	EF	UNC/BU
1911	929	5,951,284	BV	£15	£40	£80/£120
1911	930	6,007 Proofs			£40	£100/£200
1912	931	8,571,731	BV	£15	£60	£150/
1913	932	4,545,278	£9	£25	£60	£200/
1914*	933	21,252,701	BV	£14	£25	£70/£100
1915	934	12,367,939	BV	£14	£40	£80/£100
1916	935	21,064,337	BV	£14	£30	£60/£90
1917	936	11,181,617	BV	£14	£35	£60/
1918	937	29,211,792	BV	£14	£30	£70/£90
1919	938	9,469,292	BV	£18	£30	£65/£100

GEORGE V .500 silver, 28.5mm

Date	ESC	Mintage	Fine	VF	EF	UNC/BU
1920	ND	Deeper engraved bust	BV	£12	£50	£120/
1920*	939	15,387,833	BV	£9	£30	£80/£100
1921	940	34,863,895	BV	£8	£35	£65/£90
1922	941	23,861,044	BV	£6	£30	£55/£70
1923	942	21,546,533	BV	£6	£25	£60/£80
1923	ND	1 of BRITT points to tooth	GVF/NEF: £150 (2006)			
1924	943	4,582,372	BV	£10	£35	£80/£100
1925	944	1,404,136	£20	£50	£300	£400/£500
1926	945	5,125,410	BV	£15	£50	£80/£120
1927	947	15,000 Proofs of new design				£100/£120
1928	948	11,087,186	BV	£4	£10	£25/£40
1929	949	16,397,279	BV	£4	£10	£25/£40
1930	950	5,753,568	BV	£8	£20	£60/£90
1931	951	6,556,331	BV	£4	£15	£40/£50
1932	952	717,041	£20	£100	£300	£1000/
1933	953	8,685,303	BV	£3	£15	£30/£40
1935	954	7,540,546	BV	£3	£6	£14/£30
1936	955	9,897,448	BV	£3	£5	£14/£25

George V 1911 Florin

*1914 Large rim teeth or small rim teeth reported.

* 1920 'BRITT' has either 'I' pointing directly at, or between rim beads. Both varieties are rarely distinguished.

George V 1936
2nd Type Florin, 1927-36

EDWARD VIII .500 silver, 28.5mm. As George VI but with ER initials.
The planned reverse was the George VI type - with ER instead of GR - designed by George Kruger Gray. The obverse was by Thomas Humphrey Paget. This was not officially issued.

Date	ESC	Mintage	VF	EF	UNC/BU
1937	955A	3-4 Examples known.	Very expensive!		

GEORGE VI .500 silver (until 1946), 28.5mm. Weight 11.33g.
Thomas Humphrey Paget designed the bust of George VI. The reverse was the work of George Kruger Gray.

Date	ESC	Mintage	VF	EF	UNC/BU
1937	956	13,006,781	BV	£3	£8/£12
1937	957	26,402 Proofs			£12/£20
1938	958	7,909,388	£3	£7	£30/£40
1939	959	20,850,607	BV	£4	£6/£10
1940	960	18,700,338	BV	£3	£10/£15
1941	961	24,451,079	BV	£3	£9/£15
1942	962	39,895,243	BV	£3	£5/£10
1943	963	26,711,987	BV	£3	£6/£10
1944	964	27,560,005	BV	£3	£5/£10
1945	965	25,858,049	BV	£3	£5/£10
1946	966	22,910,085	BV	£3	£5/£10

Now Cupro-Nickel (no silver), 28.5mm. Weight 11.3g.

Date	ESC	Mintage	VF	EF	UNC/BU
1947	967	22,910,085		£1	£5/£10
1948	968	67,553,636		£1	£5/£10
1949	968A	28,614,939		£1	£10/£20
1950	968B	24,357,490		£2	£10/£20
1950	968C	17,513 Proofs			£20/
1951	968D	27,411,747		£3	£10/£20
1951	968E	20,000 Proofs			£20/

George VI 1937 Florin.
IND:IMP was removed in 1949.

ELIZABETH II Cupro-Nickel (no silver), 28.5mm. Weight 11.5g
The bust was by Mary Gillick, the reverse was the work of Edgar Fuller, modelled by Cecil Thomas. As with the other denominations, the 1953 coins usually have poorly defined details on the head. The dies were improved for the 1954 issue onwards. In 1954 the title BRITT OMN was removed from the coins.

Date	ESC	Mintage	EF	UNC/BU
1953	968F	11,958,710		£5/£6
1953	968G	40,000 Proofs		£10/£12
1954	968H	13,085,422	£10	£30/£40
1955	968I	25,887,253		£5/£8
1956	968J	47,824,500		£5/£8
1957	968K	33,071,282	£5	£35/£55
1958	968L	9,564,580	£5	£20/£30
1959	968M	14,080,319	£5	£25/£35
1960	968N	13,831,782		£4/£5
1961	968O	37,735,315		£4/£5
1962	968P	35,147,903		£3/£4
1963	968Q	25,562,000		£3/£4
1964	968R	16,539,000		£2/£4
1965	968S	48,163,000		£1/£3
1966	968T	84,041,000		£1/£2
1967*	968U	39,718,000		£1/£2
1967	ND	Double tails error		?
1970	968V	Proofs 750,476 from set		£3/£4

*1967 Mintage figure includes over 17 million struck in 1968 but dated 1967

Elizabeth II 1965 Florin. The 1953 Florins had BRITT:OMN in the obverse legend.

GEORGE III .925 fine silver, 32mm. Weight 14.1g
The last Half Crowns issued for circulation before 1816 were dated 1751 (George II), although Spanish coins were counter-marked with the bust of George III to supply the demand until the re-coinage of 1816. Thomas Wyon junior (cousin of William Wyon) was responsible for the first head, which became known as the 'Bull' head. The King didn't like it, and it was changed in 1817 to a Pistrucci version. Thomas Wyon designed the first half crown reverse, the second was a modified version.

Date	ESC	Mintage	Fine	VF	EF	UNC/BU
1st 'Bull' style head						
1816	613		£25	£75	£250	£450/
1817	616	8,092,656	£20	£60	£300	£500/
1817	616A	'D' of 'DEI' over 'T'	£100			
1817	ND	E of DEF over R&E	£400			
1817	ND	S of PENSE over I	£200			

2nd Type, with re-designed smaller head and new reverse.						
1817	618	Included above	£20	£65	£250	
1817	618A	S's in motto mirrored			Very Rare	
1818	621	2,905,056	£20	£80	£300	£600/
1819	623	4,790,016	£20	£60	£270	£500/
1819	ND	9 Struck over 8		£900	Adams/Spink 2005	
1819	ND	HO & SO over smaller ho & so	£240	Adams/Spink 2005		
1820	625	2,396,592 (Inc. GIV)	£25	£70	£300	£500/

George III 1817 1st type
'Bull Head' Half Crown

George III 1818 2nd Type Half Crown

GEORGE IV .925 fine silver, 32mm. Weight 14.1g

Benedetto Pistrucci designed the first Romanesque laureate head, but refused to copy Sir Francis Chantrey's work, and so the second bust was by Sir Francis Chantrey and was engraved by William Wyon. All three reverses were the work of Jean Baptiste Merlen. The first and second reverse types are very similar to their respective shilling reverses. The third reverse is illustrated below.

Date	ESC	Mintage	Fine	VF	EF	UNC/BU
1st Roman style Laureate bust.						
1820	628	Inc above, 1st Rev	£25	£70	£300	£600/
1821	631	1,435,104, 1st Rev	£30	£70	£300	£600/
1821*	ND	Heavier garnishing 1st Rev	£50	£120	£400	
1823	633	2,003,760 1st Rev	£1k	£3k	£8k	
1823	634	Inc above, 2nd Rev	£30	£80	£350	£700/
1824	636	465,696 ?	£40	£90	£350	£800/
2nd Bare, thinner Wyon/Chantrey bust with 3rd reverse.						
1824	639	3-4 known, 3rd Rev	Very expensive!			
1825	642	2,258,784	£35	£80	£300	£650/
1826	646	2,189,088	£35	£80	£400	£700/
1828	648	49,890 ?		£200	£800	
1829	649	508,464	£60	£100	£400	£800/

* 1821 - The reverse type with heavier shield garnishing also has the left leg of the A of ANNO pointing just to the right of a rim denticle.

George IV 1820 Half Crown (1st head)

George IV 1825 Half Crown (2nd head)

William IV 1834 Half Crown

WILLIAM IV .925 fine silver, 32mm. Weight 14.1g

Jean Baptiste Merlen designed and engraved the reverse

Date	ESC	Mintage	Fine	VF	EF	UNC/BU
1831	656	5-10 examples	Very expensive!			
1834	660	993,168 block WW	£40	£150	£550	£1000/
1834	662	WW script	£20	£70	£400	£800/
1835	665	281,952	£50	£120	£500	£1000/
1836	666	1,588,752	£30	£80	£350	£750/
1836	666A	6 over 5	£70	£200	£600	
1837	667	150,526	£60	£200	£750	£1100/

VICTORIA .925 fine silver, 32mm. Weight 14.1g

W Wyon designed and engraved the young head of Queen Victoria. In 1874 the design was modified and struck in lower relief. J B Merlen designed and engraved the reverse.

Date	ESC	Mintage	Fine	VF	EF	UNC/BU
Young Head:						
1839	668	WW raised	£750	£1500	£6000	
1839	672	WW incuse		£13.5k (2017)		
1840	673	386,496	£70	£200	£550	£1000/
1841	674	42,768	£700	£2k	£4k	
1842	675	486,288	£70	£100	£600	£1000/
1843	676	454,608	£100	£300	£1500	£3000/
1844	677	1,999,008	£50	£120	£550	£1400/
1845	679	2,231,856	£40	£100	£550	£1200/
1846	680	1,539,668	£50	£120	£550	£1200/
1846	ND	8 over 6	£500	Adams/Spink 2005		
1848	681	Irregular obv lettering		£3500		
1848*	681A	367,488. 8/6		£2000		
1848	ND	8 over 7	£400?			
1849	682	261,360 large date		£200	£750	
	683	Small date	£100	£300	£900	
	ND	9 over 7 (or double struck 9) Fine: £200				
1850	684	484,613	£60	£200	£650	£1800/
1874	692	2,188,599	£25	£70	£220	£500/
1875	696	1,113,483	£20	£70	£250	£550/
1876	699	633,221	£30	£100	£400	£900/
	699A	6 over 5	£50			
1877	700	447,059	£25	£40	£200	£500/
1878	701	1,466,232	£25	£50	£250	£500/
1879	703	901,356	£30	£100	£300	£550/
1880	705	1,346,350	£25	£60	£250	£500/
1881	707	2,301,495	£25	£60	£200	£500/
1882	710	808,227	£30	£100	£250	£550/
1883	711	2,982,779	£20	£65	£250	£450/
1884	712	1,569,175	£20	£65	£200	£450/
1885	713	1,628,438	£20	£65	£200	£450/
1886	715	891,767	£20	£65	£200	£450/
1887	717	261,747	£35	£100	£250	£450/

Victoria 1850 Half Crown

Victoria 1874 Half Crown obverse,
with the modified portrait

VICTORIA Jubilee head .925 fine silver, 32mm. Weight 14.1g
Sir Joseph Boehm designed the Jubilee head, which was engraved by Leonard Charles Wyon. Mr Wyon also engraved the reverse, from his own design. The old head bust was by Sir Thomas Brock, who was also responsible for the reverse design. Both sides of the old head half crown were engraved by George William de Saulles.

Date	ESC	Mintage	Fine	VF	EF	UNC/BU
1887	719	1,176,299	£10	£20	£30	£60/
1887	720	1,084 Proofs				£500/
1888	721	1,428,787	£10	£20	£50	£140/
1889	722	4,811,954	£10	£20	£50	£140/
1890	723	3,228,111	£10	£20	£50	£160/
1891	724	2,284,632	£12	£25	£80	£160/
1892	725	1,710,946	£14	£20	£80	£160/
Old, Veiled, or Widow Head type:						
1893	726	1,792,600	£10	£20	£50	£100/
1893	727	1,312 Proofs				£500/
1894	728	1,524,960	£12	£20	£100	£200/
1895	729	1,772,662	£16	£30	£80	£200/
1896	730	2,148,505	£14	£20	£75	£200/
1897	731	1,678,643	£14	£20	£70	£180/
1898	732	1,870,055	£14	£20	£75	£200/
1899	733	2,863,872	£14	£20	£50	£160/
1900	734	4,479,128	£14	£25	£60	£140/
1901	735	1,516,570	£14	£20	£50	£120/

Victoria Jubilee Head 1887 Half Crown

Victoria Veiled Head 1893 Half Crown

EDWARD VII .925 fine silver, 32mm. Weight 14.14g

Both obverse and reverse were the work of George William de Saulles.

Date	ESC	Mintage	Fine	VF	EF	UNC/BU
1902	746	1,316,008	£20	£35	£75	£140/
1902	747	15,123 Matt Proofs				£200/
1903	748	274,840	£150	£500	£2000	
1904	749	709,652	£70	£200	£750	£1500/
1905	750	166,008	£500	£1500	£5k	£10k/
1906	751	2,886,206	£20	£50	£250	£600/
1907	752	3,693,930	£20	£50	£200	£600/
1908	753	1,758,889	£25	£75	£400	£1000/
1909	754	3,051,592	£20	£50	£300	£750/
1910	755	2,557,685	£20	£50	£250	£400/

Edward VII 1909 Half Crown

GEORGE V .925 fine silver (until 1920), 32mm. Weight 14.14g

The obverse is by Sir Bertram MacKennal (which was modified at various stages) and the first reverse design is a slightly modified version of the Edward VII type. From 1927 onwards a different reverse was used, this was designed by George Kruger Gray.

The early George V half crowns (and other contemporary denominations) are very hard to grade accurately. They often look EF, even when in actual fact they are UNC, or very near so. I find the key is to look closely at the surfaces for traces of loss of lustre, which in hand, can sometimes be a better indication of wear than the lack of detail due to other factors. From pictures alone they are even harder to grade, and that may explain some recent increases in prices for EF - i.e. the coins may be described as EF, but are actually better than the EF examples in potential buyer's collections and therefore sell for more.

Date	ESC	Mintage	Fine	VF	EF	UNC/BU
1911	757	2,914,573	BV	£20	£70	£150/
1911	758	6,007 Proofs				£250/
1912	759	4,700,789	BV	£20	£60	£200/
1913	760	1,090,160	£10	£25	£80	£250/
1914	761	18,333,003	BV	£14	£35	£80/
1915	762	32,433,066	BV	£10	£35	£80/
1916	763	29,530.020	BV	£10	£40	£80/
1917	764	11,172.052	BV	£10	£40	£80/
1918	765	29,079,592	BV	£10	£40	£80/
1919	766	10,266,737	BV	£10	£35	£80/

George V 1917 Half Crown

GEORGE V Debased .500 silver, 32mm. Weight 14.14g:

Date	ESC	Mintage	Fine	VF	EF	UNC/BU
1920	767	17,983,077	BV	£10	£40	£100/
1920	ND	Small head, high relief Obv 1/Rev B (2001) BU £110				
1921	768	23,677,889	BV	£10	£40	£100/
1922*	769	16,396,774 Rev A	BV	£10	£30	£100/
	ND	Rev B	BV	£10	£30	£100/
1923	770	26,308,526	BV	£7	£25	£70/
1924	771	5,866,294	BV	£8	£40	£90/
1925	772	1,413,461	£20	£70	£300	£600/
1926	773	4,473,516	BV	£25	£60	£140/
1926	773A	No colon after OMN	?			
1926	774	Mod Effigy (Appendix I)	BV	£20	£50	£150/
1927	775	6,852,872	BV	£10	£30	£70/
1927	776	15,000 Proofs of New design				£80/
1928	777	18,762,727 (minor varieties)	BV	£8	£15	£45/
1929	778	17,632,636 (minor varieties)	BV	£8	£15	£35/
1930	779	809,501	£15	£50	£250	£700/
1931	780	11,264,468	BV	£5	£15	£40/£50
1932	781	4,793,643	BV	£7	£15	£30/£50
1933	782	10,311,494	BV	£7	£10	£20/£30
1934	783	2,422,399	BV	£8	£30	£75/£100
1935	784	7,022,216	BV	£7	£15	£25/£30
1936	785	7,039,423	BV	£7	£9	£25/£30

George V 1935 Half Crown reverse.
Used 1927-1936

* 1922 - There are two different reverses encountered on 1922 half crowns. The first (A) uses the reverse of the 1921 coin, the second (B) has the reverse of the 1923 coin. Differences include: The 'F' in 'FID' points to a bead (A) or to a space (B) and the cross on top of crown points to a bead (A) or to the right of a bead (B).

EDWARD VIII, .500 silver, 32mm
The proposed reverse by George Kruger Gray featured a rectangular Royal standard flag. The obverse was by Thomas Humphrey Paget. This coin was never officially issued, and the reverse design was not used again.

Date	ESC	Mintage	Fine	VF	EF	UNC/BU
1937	785A	Royal arms Flag reverse.		Expensive!		

GEORGE VI .500 silver (until 1946), 32mm. Weight 14.14g
Thomas Humphrey Paget designed the bust of George VI. The reverse was the work of George Kruger Gray.

Date	ESC	Mintage	EF	UNC/BU
1937	786	9,106,440	BV	£15/£25
1937	787	26,402 Proofs		£30/
1938	788	6,426,478	£10	£25/£35
1939	789	15,478,635	BV	£15/£20
1940	790	17,948,439	BV	£8/£12
1941	791	15,773,984	BV	£8/£12
1942	792	31,220,090	BV	£8/£12
1942	ND	Specimen strike (also of 1943)		£100/
1943	793	15.462,875	BV	£9/£12
1944	794	15,255,165	BV	£9/£12
1945	795	19,849,242	BV	£5/£10
1946	796	22,724,873	BV	£5/£10

George VI 1945 Half Crown

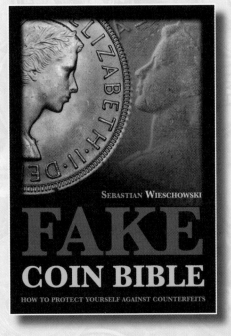

GEORGE VI Cupro-Nickel (No Silver),, 32mm. Weight 14.22g

1947	797	21,911,484	£2	£5/£10
1948	798	71,164,703	£2	£5/£10
IND: IMP legend (Emperor of India) discontinued.				
1949	798A	28,272,512	£3	£12/£20
1950	798B	28,335,500	£5	£20/£25
1950	798C	17,513 Proofs		£25/
1951	798D	9,003,520	£5	£20/£25
1951	798E	20,000 Proofs		£25/
1952	798F	1 or 2 Known	Expensive!	

ELIZABETH II Cupro-Nickel (No Silver), 32mm. Weight 14.2g
Mary Gillick designed the first bust of Elizabeth II. The reverse was the work of Edgar Fuller, modelled by Cecil Thomas.

Date	ESC	Mintage	EF	UNC/BU
1953	798G	4,333,214	£1	£8/£10
1953	798H	40,000 Proofs		£18/
1954	798I	11,614,953	£10	£40/£50
1955	798J	23,628,726	£1	£8/£12
1956	798K	33,934,909	£2	£12/£20
1957	798L	34,200,563	£2	£7/£9
1958	798M	15,745,668	£3	£25/£30
1959	798N	9,028,844	£3	£25/£30
1960	798O	19,929,191		£3/£5
1961	798P	25,887,89		£3/£5
1962	798S	24,013,312		£2/£4
1963	798T	17,557,600		£2/£4
1964	798U	5,973,600		£2/£4
1965	798V	9,878,400		£1/£3
1966	798W	13,384,000		£1/£2
1967	798X	33,058,400		£1/£2
1970	798Y	Proofs from the set		£5/£7

Elizabeth II 1966 Half Crown

GEORGE III .925 fine silver, 34-35mm. Accurate weight not known at time of writing.
The Three Shilling was another short token issue, struck under the authority of the Bank of England in order to provide much needed change until the major re-coinage of 1816. Two bust types were used on these during their short run. The first bust is the military type as shown below, the second bust was a laureate head type, as shown on the EIGHTEEN PENCE token page. There are five non proof varieties of 1811, and six different proof types! The die varieties can be identified using: on the obverse, the front leaf of the laurel and its relationship with the 'E' of 'DEI', and on the reverse, the number of acorns in the oak wreath:

Type 1 = Obv: front leaf points to end of 'E'. Rev: has 27 acorns present.
Type 2 = Obv: front leaf points to end of 'E'. Rev: has 26 acorns present.
Type 3 = Obv: front leaf points to gap between 'D' and 'E'. Rev: has 26 acorns present.
Type 4 = Obv: front leaf points to gap between 'D' and 'E'. Rev: has 25 acorns present.
Type 5 = Obv: front leaf points to the upright of 'E'. Rev: has 24 acorns present.

Date	ESC	Mintage or Details	Fine	VF	EF	UNC/BU
1811	407	Type 1(Scarce)	£20	£60	£200	
1811	408	Type 2(Commonest)	£20	£60	£120	
1811	410	Type 3(Rarer)	£20	£70	£150	
1811	411	Type 4(Rarer)	?			
1811	413	Type 5(Rarer)	?			
1812	415	(1st head)	£20	£70	£150	£250/
1812	416	(2nd head from here)	£20	£70	£150	£250/
1813	421		£20	£70	£150	
1814	422		£20	£70	£150	
1815	423		£20	£70	£150	
1816	424			£300	£600	£1500/

Double Florin

VICTORIA .925 fine silver, 36mm. Weight 22.62g
Sir Joseph Boehm designed the Jubilee head, which was engraved by Leonard Charles Wyon. Mr Wyon also engraved the reverse, from his own design. The denomination was not popular, as it was often confused for a crown and became known as the 'barmaids ruin'.

Date	ESC	Mintage or Details	Fine	VF	EF	UNC/BU
1887	394	483,347 Roman I	£20	£30	£65	£120/
1887	395	Arabic 1 in date	£20	£30	£60	£100/
1888	397	243,340	£25	£40	£90	£140/
1888*	397A	Inverted 1 VICTORIA	£30	£50	£175	£400/
1889	398	1,185,111	£20	£25	£90	£150/
1889*	398A	Inverted 1 VICTORIA	£30	£45	£175	£400/
1890	399	782,146	£20	£40	£90	£150/

* The second 'I' in 'VICTORIA' appears to be an upside-down digit '1'. It is in fact a damaged letter '1'.

George III Three Shilling Bank Token. On the obverse, the front leaf of the laurel points to the gap between the 'D' and 'E'.

Right: Queen Victoria 1887 Double Florin reverse. The obverse is similar to the half crown, which also with the legend 'VICTORIA DEI GRATIA.

There are two slightly different obverse types noted for the 'Arabic' 1887 coin. The easiest way to spot them concerns the 'D' of 'DEI' and exactly to which bead in the Crown it is level with. Both types seem to be common.

Bank of England Five Shilling token

GEORGE III .925 fine silver, 41mm. Accurate weight not known at time of writing.
The largest denomination of the Bank of England token issues. The Dollar started life with a face value of five shillings, but did rise to five shillings and sixpence for six years, while silver was in short supply. All are dated 1804, although they were struck up to 1811 and remained legal tender until 1820, by which time their face value was back to five shillings. There are seventeen proof varieties of this coin in various metals, and ten non proof varieties, which are a result of slightly different obverse and reverse die combinations being used. They were struck on Spanish/Spanish colonial Pieces of Eight and coins with lots of Spanish detail, especially dates and mintmarks do attract a premium.

Type 1 = Obv: front leaf points to upright of 'E'. Rev: raised 'K' under shield.
Type 2 = Obv: front leaf points to upright of 'E'. Rev: inverted incuse 'Я'.
Type 3 = Obv: as above, but no stops between CHK on neck. Rev: raised 'K' under shield.
Type 4 = Obv: as 1 but leaf points to centre of 'E'. Rev: raised 'K' under shield.
Type 5 = Obv: as 1 but leaf points to centre of 'E'. Rev: inverted raised 'Я'
Type 6 = Obv: as 1 but leaf points to centre of 'E'. Rev: inverted incuse 'Я'.
Type 7 = Obv: as 1 but leaf points to right end of 'E'. Rev: raised 'K' under shield.
Type 8 = Obv: as 1 but leaf points to right end of 'E'. Rev: inverted raised 'Я'
Type 9 = Obv: as 1 but leaf points to right end of 'E'. Rev: inverted incuse 'Я'.
Type 10 = Obv: no stop after REX, leaf to centre of 'E'. Rev: raised 'K' under shield.

Date	ESC	Type	Fine	VF	EF
1804	144	Type 1 (commonest)	£120	£200	£300
1804	147	Type 2 (very rare)	?		
1804	148	Type 3 (rare)	£150	£300	
1804	149	Type 4 (scarce)	£150	£350	
1804	153	Type 5 (rare)	?		
1804	156	Type 6 (scarce)	£180	£350	
1804	158	Type 7 (ext. rare)	?		
1804	159	Type 8 (very rare)	?		
1804	162	Type 9 (very rare)	?		
1804	164	Type 10 (common)	£200	£300	

George III Dollar Bank Token. On the
obverse, the front leaf points to the
centre of the 'E'.

GEORGE III .925 fine silver, 37.6mm. Weight 28.2759g
Prior to this issue the last crown struck for circulation was dated 1751 (George II). Dies were designed and engraved by Benedetto Pistrucci. This was the first time a St George and the Dragon design had been used since the reign of Henry VIII.

Date	Edge	ESC	Mintage	Fine	VF	EF	UNC/BU
1818	LVIII	211	155,232	£40	£100	£400	£800/
1818*	LVIII	213A	Error edge	?			
1818	LIX	214	Inc above	£40	£100	£500	
1819	LIX	215	683,496	£40	£100	£450	
1819	LIX	215A	No stops on edge	£50	£200	£500	
1819	LIX	215B	9 over 8	£100	£200	£600	
1819	LX	216	Inc above	£40	£100	£400	
1819*	LX	ND	TVTAMEN	?			
1820	LX	219	448,272	£50	£100	£400	£900/
1820	LX	220A	20 over 19		£200		
1820	LX	ND	S over T (Soit)	?			

* 1818 Error edge reads: DECVS ANNO REGNI ET TVTAMEN.
* 1819 No stop after the word TVTAMEN.

George III 1818 Crown

George IV 1821 Crown

GEORGE IV .925 fine silver, Laureate Roman style head 37.6mm. Weight 28.2759g
The obverse and reverse were designed by Benedetto Pistrucci and engraved by Jean Baptiste Merlen.

Date	Edge	ESC	Mintage	Fine	VF	EF	UNC/BU
1821	SEC*	246	437,976	£50	£200	£800	£1500/
1822	SEC*	251	124,929	£50	£250	£800	£2000/
1822	TER*	252	Inc Above	£50	£200	£800	£1800/

* SEC = SECUNDO, TER= TERTIO - Regnal year on the edge.

WILLIAM IV .925 fine silver, 38mm. No William IV Crowns were issued for general circulation.

VICTORIA .925 fine silver Young Head, 38mm. Weight approx 28.35g
William Wyon produced the Young head Victoria portrait. The reverse was the work of Jean Baptiste Merlen, just before his retirement in 1844.

Date	Edge	ESC	Mintage	Fine	VF	EF	UNC/BU
1844	VIII	280	94,248 Star stops	£50	£120	£800	
1844	VIII	281	Cinquefoil stops*	£60	£100	£900	
1845	VIII	282A	159,192 Star stops	£60	£150	£1000	£2500/
1845	VIII	ND	Star stops, error edge, reads: AANNO			£2000	
1845	VIII	282	Cinquefoil stops*	£60	£150	£900	£2500/
1847	XI	286	140,976	£70	£150	£900	£2500/
1847**	UNDECIMO		ESC 288*, 8,000 All Proofs	£700	£2000	£5000/

* A cinquefoil is a pattern of five leaves.
** The Gothic Crown wasn't a circulation issue, but is included here for completeness.

Above: Victoria Young Head 1845 Crown.

VICTORIA .925 fine silver Jubilee Head, 38.6mm.. Weight approx 28.35g
Sir Joseph Boehm designed the Jubilee head, which was engraved by Leonard Charles Wyon. The reverse on both the jubilee head crown and the old head crown is the classic Benedetto Pistrucci St George slaying the dragon design. The old head bust was by Sir Thomas Brock. A regnal edge year was used on the old head crown, and because Victoria was not crowned on January 1st, this results in two different regnal year types for each date.

Date	ESC	Mintage	Fine	VF	EF	UNC/BU
1887	296	173,581	£25	£35	£80	£150/
1887	297	1,084 Proofs			£600	
1888	298	131,899 Close date	£25	£35	£100	£200/
1888	ND	Wide date	£90	£200	£400	
1889	299	1,807,223	£25	£35	£80	£200/
1890	300	997,862	£25	£38	£100	£200/
1891	301	566,394	£25	£38	£100	£250/
1892	302	451,334	£30	£45	£150	£300/

Victoria 1887 Jubilee Head Crown

VICTORIA .925 fine silver Old, Veiled or Widow Head, 38.6mm.. Weight approx 28.35g

Date	Edge	ESC	Mintage	Fine	VF	EF	UNC/BU
1893	LVI	303	497,845	£25	£35	£150	£300/
1893	LVI	304	1,312 Proofs			£500	£1200/
1893	LVII	305	Inc Above	£30	£70	£200	£300/
1894	LVII	306	144,906	£25	£50	£150	£300/
1894	LVIII	307	Inc Above	£25	£50	£150	£300/
1895	LVII	308	252,862	£25	£50	£150	£300/
1895	LIX	309	Inc Above	£25	£60	£150	£300/
1896	LIX	310	317,599	£25	£50	£150	£300/
1896	LX	311	Inc Above	£25	£50	£150	£300/
1897	LX	312	262,118	£25	£50	£150	£300/
1897	LXI	313	Inc Above	£25	£50	£150	£300/
1898	LXI	314	161,450	£35	£100	£300	£400/
1898	LXII	315	Inc Above	£25	£40	£150	£300/
1899	LXII	316	166,300	£25	£40	£150	£300/
1899	LXIII	317	Inc Above	£25	£40	£150	£300/
1900	LXIII	318	353,356	£25	£40	£120	£300/
1900	LXIV	319	Inc Above	£25	£60	£120	£300/

Queen Victoria Veiled Head 1893 Crown

Edward VII 1902 Crown. (Reverse type was the same as the Veiled Head Victorian crowns)

EDWARD VII .925 fine silver, 38.6mm.. Weight approx 28.35g

A one year only issue, and the very last British crown made for circulation (the later ones being commemorative/special issues only). The bust is by George William de Saulles and the reverse is the St George type by Benedetto Pistrucci.

Date	Edge	ESC	Mintage	Fine	VF	EF	UNC/BU
1902	II	361	256,020	£50	£100	£170	£250/
1902	II	362	15,123 Matt Proofs			£200	£300/

GEORGE V .500 silver, 38.6mm. Weight approx 28.4g

In 1927 the mint decided to produce proof sets of the newly designed coinage. The crown, among other coins, was produced as a proof striking only, to be sold in these sets. The design was popular, so subsequently a small number of crowns were struck annually, mainly to provide the public with keepsakes, which were often given as gifts at Christmas time. The popular 'Wreath' crown was produced annually (except 1935) until the death of the king in 1936. In 1935 to celebrate the king's Silver Jubilee a larger number of special crowns were struck featuring an Art Deco St George slaying the dragon. The bust on both coins was the standard Bertram MacKennal design. The wreath reverse was by George Kruger Gray, and the jubilee crown reverse was by Percy Metcalfe. Many have criticized the Art Deco St George on the 1935 crown, but personally I think it looks classic 1930s, and makes a nice change from the Pistrucci version. The king himself had mixed feelings, saying that St George looked 'A damned bad rider'. The design was approved, so he couldn't have entirely hated it.

Date	Edge	ESC	Mintage	Fine	VF	EF	UNC/BU
1927		367	15,030 Proofs			£160	£250/£320
1928		368	9,034	£100	£150	£300	£350/
1929		369	4,994	£100	£150	£330	£400/
1930		370	4,847	£120	£160	£350	£450/
1931		371	4,056	£100	£160	£320	£400/
1932		372	2,395	£200	£300	£550	£700/
1933		373	7,132	£100	£160	£250	£400/
1934		374	932	£1200	£2000	£3000	£4000/£5000
1935*		375	714,769 incuse edge	£10	£20	£30/	
1935*		375A	Error edge lettering**		£900		
1935*		376	SPECIMEN striking, in original box				£50/£60
1936		381	2,473	£150	£300	£500	£750/

Images below, Left to right - The obverse and reverse of a 1928 Wreath Crown. The last image is the reverse of the 1935 Crown. The 1935 Crown obverse was similar to that of the Wreath Crown.

* The 1935 coins all feature the George slaying the dragon reverse, not the wreath type reverse.
**The non proof 1935 error edge has a large space after 'ANNO' and some missing letters.

EDWARD VIII .500 silver, 38.6mm

Date	ESC	Mintage	VF	EF	UNC/BU
1937	391C	Reverse as George VI 1937.			Very rare

GEORGE VI .500 silver, 38.6mm . Weight approx 28.2g
The bust for all George VI coins was by Thomas Humphrey Paget. The reverse of the coronation coin was by George Kruger Gray. The reverse of the 1951 Festival of Britain coin was created by re-using an 1899 crown die with a manually adjusted date. The Festival of Britain crown boxes exist as either matchbox/slide open style, or as boxes with a lift off lid. Coins in green boxes are a little less common.

Date	ESC	Mintage	VF	EF	UNC/BU
1937	392	418,699 Coronation	£10	£20	£30/£40
1937	393	26,402 Proofs from the sets			£50/£90

Cupro-Nickel (No silver), 38.6mm. Struck for the Festival of Britain in 1951.

Date	ESC	Mintage	VF	EF	UNC/BU
1951	393C	1,983,540 Highly prooflike		£5	£7/£10
1951		In box of issue, green or purple		£6	£10/£12
1951	ND	Error edge lettering - Blundered Latin date and large space before 'FLORET' [Predecimal.com 2006]			£300/
1951	ND	Error edge lettering - partial overlapping			£200/

The reverse of the 1937 Crown (obv is similar to the 1951 Crown, but with 'FIVE SHILLINGS' under the bust).

1951 Crown - The reverse used for these was a re-cycled 1899 Crown die with the date changed by hand

Queen Elizabeth II 1953 Crown

ELIZABETH II Cupro-Nickel (No silver), 38.6mm . Weight 28.2g (28.4g 1965)
The coronation crown was an interesting departure from tradition, featuring the monarch on horseback; the first time this had been done since the reign of Charles I. Gilbert Ledward designed the obverse and the reverse was a joint effort by Edgar Fuller and Cecil Thomas. The edge has the words 'FAITH AND TRUTH I WILL BEAR UNTO YOU'. The New York Trades fair and Churchill crowns have the young bust by Mary Gillick. The Trades Fair crown uses the same reverse as the coronation crown. The reverse of the Churchill crown was modelled from a bust by Croatian artist Oscar Nemon. The actual bust, which is now part of the Government Art Collection looks much better than the quite low relief design on the much criticized crown.

Date	ESC	Mintage	VF	EF	UNC/BU
1953	393F	5,962,621		£3	£4/£7
1953	393G	40,000 Proofs		£15	£20/£30
1953	ND	(Hip Hop) Edge Error: "...WILL BEAR UNTO YO" (no 'U')			
			£30	£40	£60/£80
1960	393K	1,024,038 British Trades Fair issue		£4	£6/£10
1960	393L	70,000 Polished die specials in box		£7	£20/£25
1965	393N	19,640,000 Churchill issue		25p	75p/£1

From left to right: The obverse of the 1960 Crown (Reverse type was as the 1953 Crown). Obv and Rev of the 1965 Churchill Crown.

Guinea based denominations 1797 - 1815

Introduced in 1663 to coincide with a full range of new milled coins that replaced their hammered (hand struck) predecessors, the guinea and it's fractions and multiples circulated until 1815. Most of the early guineas were made of gold from Guinea in West Africa, hence the name. Originally the guinea had a face value of 20 shillings but fluctuations in the price of gold led the government to fix the face value at 21 shillings, or £1 and 1 shilling (nowadays £1.05 in decimal) from 1717 until it was replaced by the sovereign 100 years later.

Despite the fact that the last actual guinea coin was struck in 1813, the term 'guinea' to represent 21 shillings was used in accounting and on price lists and advertisements etc right up to the introduction of decimal coins in 1971. In fact, the 'guinea' lives on in horse racing circles and most importantly, it is still used as the denomination of choice for the retail price of this price guide!

Under the reign of George III, guineas and half guineas were struck throughout the reign with very few years omitted and over 7 different bust types! The third guinea coin was introduced in 1797. During the reign of George III the large five guinea and two guinea denominations were issued as patterns only and are therefore not included. A quarter guinea was also struck in 1762.

The guinea was struck with a weight of about 8.4 grammes and just like the sovereign, they are made of 22ct (916.667 parts per 1000) gold. The half guinea is logically 4.2 grammes and the third guinea therefore about 2.8 grammes.

Forgeries are sometimes encountered but it should also be brought to the readers attention that brass imitation guineas were made in very large numbers by the Victorians for use as gaming counters. Mainly as either guinea or half guinea replicas. These were made after the guinea based coins were de-monetised and were never intended to deceive. Often they have an altered reverse legend which usually features an abbreviation of the makers company name by way of advertisement. Novices sometimes assume the brass replicas to be the real thing. They are easy to differentiate as they were never as well made as the real thing and, being brass, are very much lighter.

The Quarter Guinea, approx. 15.5mm

Date	Notes	F	VF	EF
1762		£200	£350	£500

The Third Guinea, approx. 17mm

Drawing of the 1762 third guinea, by Mr F J Lees (1884).

Date	Notes	F	VF	EF
1797	1st bust, date in legend	£120	£200	£450
1798		£120	£200	£450
1799		£120	£300	£450
1800		£140	£200	£450
1801	Date under crown	£140	£200	£450
1802		£140	£200	£450
1803		£150	£200	£450
1804	2nd bust from here	£150	£200	£450
1806		£150	£200	£450
1808		£150	£200	£450
1809		£150	£200	£450
1810		£150	£200	£450
1811		£400	£800	£1200
1813		£300	£500	£900

1803 Third Guinea   1810 Third Guinea

The Half Guinea, approx. 21mm
The 3rd obverse bust causes confusion. It was short-lived, only being used for coins dated 1774 and 1775, but it seems to have been used in parallel with the last coins struck using bust 2 and with the first struck with bust 4.

Date	Notes	F	VF	EF
1762	1st bust...	£500	£1000	£2500
1763		£700	£1500	£3000
1764	2nd bust...	£400	£1000	
1765		£500		
1766		£250	£600	£1200
1768		£250	£500	
1769		£300	£600	
1772		Very rare		
1773		£300	£600	£1500
1774		£200	£350	£600
1774	3rd bust	£200	£350	£600
1775	2nd bust	£200	£350	£600
1775	3rd bust	£700		
1775	4th bust...	£250	£400	£600
1776		£200	£400	£600
1777		£200	£400	£600
1778		£250	£500	£800
1779		£250	£500	£800
1781		£200	£400	£700
1783		£400	£1000	
1784		£200	£400	£700
1785		£200	£400	£700
1786		£200	£400	£700
1787	5th bust and spade type reverse...	£200	£300	£700
1788		£200	£300	£700
1789		£200	£400	£750
1790		£200	£400	£750
1791		£200	£400	£750
1792		Rare		
1793		£200	£400	£700
1794		£200	£400	£700
1795		£200	£400	£700
1796		£200	£400	£700
1797		£200	£400	£700
1798		£200	£400	£700
1798	8 struck over a 7	£220	£450	£800
1800		£250	£600	£1200
1801	6th bust...	£200	£300	£600
1802		£200	£300	£600
1803		£200	£300	£600
1804	7th bust...	£200	£300	£500
1805		Rare		
1806		£200	£350	£600
1808		£200	£350	£600
1809		£200	£350	£600
1810		£200	£350	£550
1811		£350	£500	£900
1813		£300	£400	£700

1808 Half Guinea

The Guinea, approx. 23.5mm
Fifth bust guineas are also known as 'Spade' guineas, owing to the shape of the shield on the reverse.

Date	Notes	F	VF	EF
1761	1st bust	£1600		
1763	2nd bust...	£1000	£3500	
1764		£1000	£3500	
1764	No stop above head	£2000		
1765	3rd bust...	£350	£550	£1400
1766		£350	£550	£1400
1767		£400	£600	£2000
1768		£350	£550	£1200
1769		£350	£600	£1400
1770		£1200		
1771		£350	£550	£1000
1772		£350	£550	£1000
1773		£350	£550	£1200
1773	First 7 struck over a 1	£400	£700	
1774	4th bust...	£400	£600	£1000
1775		£400	£600	£1000
1776		£400	£600	£1000
1777		£500	£750	£1300
1778		£500	£1000	
1779		£400	£600	£1000
1781		£400	£600	£1000
1782		£400	£600	£1000
1783		£400	£600	£1000
1784		£400	£600	£1000
1785		£400	£600	£1000
1786		£400	£600	£1000
1787	5th bust...	£350	£500	£800
1788		£350	£500	£800
1789		£350	£500	£800
1790		£350	£500	£800
1791		£350	£500	£800
1792		£350	£500	£800
1793		£350	£500	£800
1794		£350	£500	£800
1795		£350	£500	£800
1796		£350	£550	£900
1797		£350	£550	£1000
1798		£350	£500	£800
1798	8 struck over a 7	£350	£500	£1000
1799		£350	£600	£1200
1813	Military (6th) bust	£700	£1700	£3500

Drawings of the first, third and
fourth busts by F J Lees.

1790 Guinea. Reverse enlarged to the right.

Sovereign based denominations 1816 - 1968

An act of parliament was implemented on the 3rd August 1816, stating that new gold coins were to be minted to replace the guinea and its fractions. The new sovereigns were given a face value of 20 shillings (one pound Sterling) and the half sovereigns were logically worth 10 shillings. The new coins were all struck using machinery installed at the new Tower Hill site, which until a few years previous, had been occupied by tobacco warehouses.

The sovereign, being a new denomination and smaller (the sovereign is just over 22mm, the half sovereign 19.5mm) than the established Guinea, was not popular at first. The government stuck with it and popularity soon grew. Almost 200 years later, the sovereign has established itself as one of the most popular gold coins in the world.

Benedetto Pistrucci came up with idea of having a Saint George motif on the reverse. At that time his artistic reputation had gained him quite a celebrity status and he was commissioned to design the Saint George and the bust of King George III for use on the new coins. As if that wasn't enough, he was also given the task of engraving the dies for the coins too.

Gold, being quite inert, tends to stay bright and for that reason the BU grade is not shown. Gold is heavy too and quite soft, so is more prone to being marked and scratched. Problems with the eye appeal will of course negatively affect the value. **At the time of writing (November 2017) the bullion content of a sovereign is worth £225.50 (half that for a half sovereign).** Gold prices fluctuate of course, so the internet or a newspaper should be checked for the current rate.

Specifications: All full sovereigns weigh 7.98 grammes and have a diameter of 22.05mm. Half sovereigns weigh 3.99 grammes and have a diameter of 19.5mm. The alloy used for both coins is 916.667 parts per 1000 gold (22 carat) which means that the gold content of an unworn and undamaged sovereign is 7.315 grammes and for a half sovereign 3.658 grammes.

George III

Date	Mintage/Notes	F	VF	EF	UNC
1817	2,080,197	£250	£330	£500	£1400
1818	1,030,286 / 2nd 8 over 7		£400	£700	£1500
1818	Inc. above	£250	£330	£500	£1400
1820	35,043 / Varieties exist	£200	£300	£500	£1400

Rare proofs of 1817 and 1818 exist.

George IV Laureate Head

1821	231,288 / 1st Reverse	£500	£1300	£2500	
1821	Proof	Rare			
1823	224,280 / 2nd Reverse	£200	£400	£800	
1824	591,530	£200	£330	£600	£1200
1825	761,150	£200	£330	£600	£1200

Bare head type from here down.

1826	344,830	£200	£330	£600	£1400
1826	Inc. above / *	£200	£330	£600	£1400
1826	Proof	Rare			
1827	492,014	£200	£300	£700	£1400
1827	Inc. above / *	£200	£300	£750	£1500
1828	1,244,754	£200	£300	£700	£1400
1828	Inc. above / *	£200	£330	£800	£1500

William IV

1831	Plain edge proof	Rare			
1831	Milled edge proof	Rare			
1834	133,899	£250	£450	£1000	£2000
1835	772,554	£200	£400	£800	£1500
1836	146,865	£200	£400	£800	£1600
1836	Error, struck using sixpence obv	Rare			
1837	160,207	£220	£400	£900	£1600

George III 1820 Half Sovereign

* Coins marked with an asterix were struck using a different obverse die. The border is heavier and an extra tuft of hair can be seen behind the Kings ear.

Victoria - Young Head
Commencing in this reign, gold coins were also minted at colonial mints in Australia, Canada and India. These colonial coins were given mintmarks to distinguish them, whereas London mint coins have no mintmark. The mintmarks used were capital letters. The letters and their positions will be pointed out in the listings. The mint letters and the various slightly different young head busts make this a difficult series to get to grips with. Increasingly, the market for Australian coins, and to a letter extent, London coins, prefers grading based on the US Sheldon scale and there can be big increases in value between coins in EF, normal UNC (MS60) and BU (around MS65 and higher) grades!

London mint coins with no mintmarks:

Date	Mintage / Notes	F	VF	EF	UNC
1838	273,341	£150	£200	£500	£1000
1839	1,230 / Proof only, plain or milled edge			Rare	
1841	508,835	£150	£200	£500	£1000
1842	2,223,352	£150	£200	£500	£1000
1843	1,251,762	£150	£200	£500	£1000
1844	1,127,007	£150	£220	£500	£1000
1845	887,526	£300	£600	£2000	
1846	1,063,928	£150	£190	£450	£1100
1847	982,326	£150	£190	£450	£1100
1848	410,595 / Tight date	£150	£190	£450	£1100
1848	Inc. above / 2nd 8 over 7	£220	£350	£500	
1848	Inc. above / Loose date	£160	£220	£450	
1849	845,112	£150	£190	£400	£1000
1850	179,595	£220	£450	£1400	
1851	773,573	£150	£200	£450	£1000
1852	1,377,671	£150	£200	£400	£1000
1853	2,708,796	£150	£200	£400	£1000
1853	Proof, large or small dates	Rare			
1854	1,125,144	£150	£200	£300	£1000
1855	1,120,362	£150	£200	£300	£1000
1856	2,391,909	£150	£220	£350	£1000
1856	Inc. above / 6 over 5	£150	£190	£300	£1000
1857	728,223	£150	£190	£300	£1000
1858	855,578	£150	£190	£250	£1000
1858	Inc. above / Larger 2nd head	£150	£190	£250	£900
1859	2,203,813	£150	£190	£250	£900
1860	1,131,500	£150	£190	£250	£900
1861	1,130,867	£150	£190	£250	£900
1862	Unknown / rare	£600	£1600	£5500	
1863	1,571,574	£150	£190	£250	£900
Now with die numbers below the shield					
1863	Inc. above	£140	£220	£400	£900
1864	1,758,490	£140	£180	£380	£800
1865	1,834,750	£140	£180	£380	£800
1866	2,058,776	£140	£180	£380	£800
1867	992,795	£140	£180	£380	£800
1869	1,861,764	£140	£180	£380	£800
1870	1,159,544	£150	£200	£380	£800
1870	Inc. above / With re-touched shield legend, coarser teeth.	£200	£300	£800	
1871	2,062,970	£150	£200	£400	£700
1871	Inc. above / With re-touched shield legend, coarser teeth.	£140	£320	£800	
1871	Inc. above / No die number	£250	£500		
1871	Inc. above / Nose points to 'T'	£160	£350	£900	
1872	3,248,627 / Nose points to 'T'	£140	£260	£800	

Victoria 1866 Young head Half Sovereign

Half Sovereign (continued)

Date	Mintage/Notes	F	VF	EF	UNC
1872	Inc. prev. page / Larger head	£140	£170	£350	£600
1873	1,927,050	£140	£170	£350	£600
1874	1,884,432	£140	£170	£350	£600
1875	516,240	£140	£170	£350	£600
1876	2,785,187	£140	£170	£350	£600
1876	Inc. above / Narrow hair ribbon	£170	£300	£500	
1877	2,197,482	£140	£170	£350	£600
1878	Inc. above / Narrow hair ribbon	£160	£300	£500	
1879	35,201	£160	£170	£400	£700
1880	1,009,049	£150	£200	£350	£800

No die numbers from this point onwards.

1880	1,009,149	£140	£200	£400	£700
1883	2,870,457	£140	£200	£350	£600
1884	1,133,756	£140	£200	£350	£500
1885	4,468,871	£140	£200	£350	£500
1885	5 over 3	£150	£250	£400	£800

Sydney mint coins, indicated here by an 'S' after the date and distinguished on the coin by a small 'S' under the shield.

1871S	356,000	£200	£300	£700
1872S	Unknown, inc. above	£150	£200	£400
1875S	252,000	£250	£400	£1000
1879S	94,000	£150	£200	£150
1880S	80,000 / Varieties exist	£200	£400	£1000
1881S	62,000 / Varieties exist	£150	£250	£600
1882S	52,000	£200	£300	£600
1882S	Legend close to heavy border	£1500		
1883S	220,000 / Varieties exist	£160	£200	£500
1883S	Legend close to heavy border (values up to 2x above)			
1886S	82,000	£160	£200	£450
1887S	134,000	£140	£170	£300

Melbourne mint coins, indicated here by an 'M' after the date and distinguished on the coin by a small 'M' under the shield.

1873M	165,034	£200	£300	£800
1877M	80,016	£300	£500	£1000
1877M	Inc. above / Narrow hair ribbon	£140	£250	£700
1881M	42,000	£160	£500	£3000
1882M	107,522 / Narrow hair ribbon	£140	£200	£400
1882M	Inc. above	£160	£250	£550
1884M	48,009	£200	£300	£1000
1885M	11,003	£300	£500	£2500
1886M	38,008	£140	£250	£1000
1887M	64,013	£160	£220	£1000

Victoria - Jubilee Head

London Mint Coins.

Date	Mintage/Notes	F	VF	EF	UNC
1887	871,770 / JEB on truncation	BV	BV	£140	£250
1887	Inc. above / Small close JEB	BV	£200	£300	
1887	Inc. above / no JEB	BV	£240	£350	
1890	2,266,023 / JEB on truncation	BV	£140	£350	
1890	Inc. above / no JEB	BV	£200	£300	£400
1890	Inc. above / *	BV	BV	£200	£300
1891	1,079,286	BV	£150	£300	
1891	Inc. above / *	BV	£150	£300	£400
1892	13,680,486 / JEB on truncation	£140	£150	£350	
1892	Inc. above / no JEB	BV	£140	£150	£250
1892	13,680,486 / *	BV	BV	£200	£350
1893	4,426,625 / *	BV	£150	£300	£400

Victoria 1887 Jubilee head Half Sovereign

* Coins marked with an asterix have a lower shield and a slightly spread apart date.

Sydney mint coins, indicated here by an 'S' after the date and distinguished on the coin by a small 'S' under the shield.

1887S	134,000 / Wide spaced JEB	£150	£190	£300	£1200
1887S	Inc. above / Normal JEB	£140	£190	£300	£1200
1889S	32,000 / Varieties exist	£170	£250	£500	£1800
1891S	77,000	£140	£200	£500	
1891S	Inc. above / no JEB	£130	£180	£400	£1800

Melbourne mint coins, indicated here by an 'M' after the date and distinguished on the coin by a small 'M' under the shield.

1887M	64,013 / Wide spaced JEB	£140	£250	£300	£1500
1887M	Inc. above / Close JEB	£130	£180	£280	£1600
1893M	110,024 / Varieties exist	£120	£200	£300	

Victoria - Veiled Head

The Pistrucci St George is back for now, and remains in constant use on half sovereigns right up to the present day. London mint coins are dealt with first.

Date	Mintage / Notes	F	VF	EF	UNC
1893	Inc. prev. page	BV	BV	£130	£200
1893	773 / Proof				£550
1894	3,794,591	BV	BV	£130	£200
1895	2,869,183	BV	BV	£130	£200
1896	2,946,605	BV	BV	£130	£200
1897	3,568,156	BV	BV	£130	£200
1898	2,878,527	BV	BV	£130	£200
1899	3,361,881	BV	BV	£130	£200
1900	4,307,372	BV	BV	£130	£200
1901	2,037,664	BV	BV	£130	£200

Victoria 1896 Veiled head Half Sovereign

Melbourne mint coins, indicated here by an 'M' after the date and distinguished on the coin by a small 'M' on the ground below the horses right rear hoof.

1893M	110,024	£150	£250		
1896M	218,946	£150	£200	£300	£1500
1899M	97,221	£150	£220	£350	£2000
1900M	112,920	£150	£200	£300	£1500

Perth mint coins, indicated here by a 'P' after the date and distinguished on the coin by a small 'P' on the ground below the horses right rear hoof.

1899P	Proof	Unique			
1900P	59,588	£160	£300	£500	£2000

Sydney mint coins, indicated here by an 'S' after the date and distinguished on the coin by a small 'S' on the ground below the horses right rear hoof.

1893S	125,000	£150	£200	£350	£1500
1897S	115,000	£150	£180	£250	£1400
1900S	84,000	£160	£200	£300	£1200

Edward VII

London mint coins listed first.

Date	Mintage / Notes	F	VF	EF	UNC
1902	4,244,457	BV	BV	£120	£250
1902	15,123 / Matte Proof				£350
1903	2,522,057	BV	BV	£140	£250
1904	1,717,440	BV	BV	£140	£250
1904	Inc. above / No B.P. in exergue	BV	BV	£170	£300
1905	3,023,993	BV	BV	£140	£250
1906	4,245,437	BV	BV	£140	£250
1907	4,233,421	BV	BV	£140	£250
1908	3,996,992	BV	BV	£140	£250
1909	4,010,715	BV	BV	£140	£250
1910	5,023,881	BV	BV	£140	£250

Edward VII 1909 Half Sovereign

Melbourne mint coins, indicated here by an 'M' after the date and distinguished on the coin by a small 'M' on the ground below the horses right rear hoof.

		F	VF	EF	UNC
1906M	82,042	£170	£300	£600	£2000
1907M	405,034	£150	£180	£200	£600
1908M	Inc. above	£170	£200	£400	£1000
1909M	186,904	£140	£160	£190	£600

Perth mint coins, indicated here by a 'P' after the date and distinguished on the coin by a small 'P' on the ground below the horses right rear hoof.

		F	VF	EF
1904P	Inc. below / No B.P. in exergue	£150	£260	£1000
1904P	60,030	£150	£200	£800
1908P	24,668	£400	£600	£1500
1909P	44,022	£150	£200	£500

Sydney mint coins, indicated here by an 'S' after the date and distinguished on the coin by a small 'S' on the ground below the horses right rear hoof.

		F	VF	EF	UNC
1902S	84,000	BV	£150	£300	£800
1902S	Proof		Rare		
1903S	231,000	BV	£140	£230	£300
1906S	308,000	BV	£140	£230	£300
1908S	538,000	BV	£140	£180	£250
1910S	474,000	BV	£140	£190	£250

George V, London mint coins listed first

Date	Mintage/Notes	F	VF	EF	UNC
1911	6,104,106	BV	BV	£150	£220
1911	3,764 / Proof				£400
1911	Matte proof	Rare			
1912	6,224,316	BV	BV	£150	£220
1913	6,094,290	BV	BV	£150	£220
1914	7,251,124	BV	BV	£150	£220
1915	2,042,747	BV	BV	£150	£220

George V 1912 Half Sovereign

Melbourne mint coins, indicated here by an 'M' after the date and distinguished on the coin by a small 'M' on the ground below the horses right rear hoof.

1915M	125,664		BV	BV	£150	£200

Perth mint coins, indicated here by a 'P' after the date and distinguished on the coin by a small 'P' on the ground below the horses right rear hoof.

1911P	130,373	BV	£140	£180	£400
1915P	356,207	BV	£140	£200	£400
1918P	Less than 500 known	£800			

Sydney mint coins, indicated here by an 'S' after the date and distinguished on the coin by a small 'S' on the ground below the horses right rear hoof.

1911S	252,000	BV	£140	£150	£200
1912S	278,000	BV	£140	£150	£200
1914S	322,000	BV	BV	£150	£200
1915S	892,000	BV	BV	£150	£200
1916S	448,000	BV	BV	£140	£180

Pretoria (South Africa) mint coins, indicated here by an 'SA' after the date and distinguished on the coin by a small 'SA' on the ground below the horses right rear hoof.

1923SA	655 / Proof				
1925SA	946,615	BV	BV	£150	£200
1926SA	808,540	BV	BV	£150	£200

Edward VII
Extremely rare, and not to be confused with modern fantasy patterns.

George VI
This issue was a plain edged proof only, struck in London. 5001 were struck, the odd '1' was for the King himself.

1937	5,501 / Plain edge Proof				£550

Elizabeth II - No half sovereigns issued until 1980.

George III

Date	Mintage / Notes	F	VF	EF	UNC
1817	3,235,239	£500	£700	£1500	£3000
1818	2,347,230 / Varieties exist	£800	£1200	£3500	£6000
1818	Wiry curls, slanted colon			Rare	
1819		Extremely rare			
1820	931,994	£450	£600	£1400	£2800

Rare proofs exist of 1817, 1818 and 1820. Varieties of 1820 also exist.

George III 1820 Sovereign

George IV

		F	VF	EF	UNC
1821	9,405,114	£450	£550	£1000	£2600
1822	5,356,787	£450	£600	£1000	£2600
1823	616,770	£1000	£2500	£4500	£8000
1824	3,767,904	£450	£700	£1500	£4000
1825	4,200,343 / Laureate head	£800	£1800	£4500	£8000
1825	Inc. above / Bare head	£450	£600	£1200	£2500
1826	5,724,046	£450	£600	£1200	£2200
1827	2,266,629	£450	£550	£1500	£2600
1828	386,182	£5000	£9500	£20k	
1829	2,444,652	£500	£650	£1600	£2600
1830	2,387,881	£500	£650	£1600	£2600

George IV Laureate head 1821 Sovereign

George IV Bare head 1830 Sovereign

William IV

		F	VF	EF	UNC
1831	598,547	£700	£1200	£2500	£4500
1831	WW incuse, no stops (values approximately double those shown above)				
1831	Nose points to 2nd I in BRITANNIAR Fine: £12k VF: £20k				
1832	3,737,065	£550	£750	£1500	£2800
1832	Inc. above / Nose to 2nd I in BRITANNIAR Fine: £800 VF: £1500				
1833	1,255,269	£500	£800	£1800	£3500
1835	723,441	£500	£850	£2000	£3500
1836	1,714,349	£500	£800	£1800	£3500
1836	Inc. above / N of ANNO in shield		Rare		
1837	1,172,984	£500	£700	£2000	£3500
1837	Inc. above / 3 over 8	£600	£1000	£3000	

Rare proofs exist of (GIV) 1821, 1825, 1826 and (WIV) 1830, 1831 and 1832.

William IV 1831 Sovereign

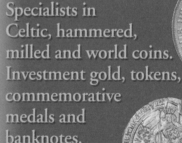

Victoria

The first coins listed here are all the shield reverse type, from the London mint.
Rare proofs exist for 1838 and 1839.

Date	Mintage/Notes	F	VF	EF	UNC
1838	2,718,694	£900	£1300	£2000	£3800
1839	503,695	£1000	£1500	£3500	£8000
1841	124,054	£4k	£7k	£10k	£20k
1842	4,865,375	£280	£300	£550	£2800
1842	Inc. above / Open 2	£330	£400	£800	£3200
1843	5,981,968	£280	£400	£600	£2000
1843	Inc. above / 2nd 3 over 2	£400	£800	£2000	£3500
1843	Inc. above / Narrow Shield	£4k	£6k	£14k	£30k
1844	3,000,445 / Large 44	£300	£400	£600	£2000
1844	Inc. above / Smaller 44	£300	£400	£1000	£2500
1844	Inc. above / date over inverted 4	Rare			
1845	3,800,845	£280	£350	£600	£1500
1845	Inc. above / date over inverted 4	Rare			
1845	Inc. above / I for 1 in date	£600	£1200		
1846	3,802,947	£280	£350	£600	£1500
1846	Inc. above / date over inverted 4	Rare			
1846	Inc. above / I for 1 in date	£600	£1200		
1847	4,667,126	£280	£350	£500	£1000
1847	Inc. above / I for 1 in date	Rare			
1848	2,246,701	£1500	£2500	£3500	£15k
1848	Inc. above / 2nd larger head	£350	£400	£550	£1400
1849	1,755,399	£350	£400	£650	£3500
1849	Inc. above / I for 1 in date	£400	£600	£1000	
1850	1,402,039	£300	£400	£500	£1800
1850	Inc. above / I for 1 in date	£300	£500	£1000	
1851	4,013,624	£280	£350	£450	£1200
1852	8,053,435	£280	£350	£450	£1000
1852	Inc. above / I for 1 in date	£300	£500	£1000	
1853	10,597,993	£280	£350	£450	£1000
1853	Inc. above / WW incuse	£350	£500	£1000	£2500
1854	3,589.611	£350	£500	£2000	£3500
1854	Inc. above / WW incuse	£300	£400	£500	£1000
1855	8,448,482	£300	£400	£1000	£2500
1855	Inc. above / WW incuse	£300	£400	£500	£1000
1856	4,806,160	£300	£350	£450	£1000
1857	4,495,748	£300	£350	£450	£1000
1858	803,234	£300	£400	£500	£1500
1859	1,547,603	£290	£320	£450	£1000
1859	Inc. above / Additional line on ribbon	£2k	£6k		
1860	2,555,958	£290	£320	£450	£1000
1860	Inc. above / large O	£270	£300	£450	£1000
1861	7,624,736	£270	£300	£400	£1000
1861	Inc. above / I for 1 in date	£350	£500	£1000	

Victoria - Young Head, shield reverse

A complicated issue with mint letter, lots of varieties and two entirely different reverses. The first coins listed here are all the shield reverse type, from the London mint.

Date	Mintage / Notes	F	VF	EF	UNC
1862	7,836,413 / Wide date	£270	£330	£450	£850
1862	Inc. above / Narrow date	£270	£330	£450	£900
1863	5,921,669	£270	£300	£350	£750
1863	Inc. above / Roman I for 1	£320	£500	£1000	
1863	'827' on truncation	Rare			

Victoria Young head, shield
back 1852 Sovereign

Die numbers below wreath until 1874

Date	Mintage / Notes	F	VF	EF	UNC
1863	Inc. above	£260	£300	£400	£850
1863	'827' on truncation, no die No.	Rare			
1864	8,656,352	£260	£200	£400	£850
1865	1,450,238	£280	£300	£450	£850
1866	4,047,288	£260	£300	£400	£850
1866	Inc. above / 2nd 6 over 5	£290	£350	£450	£900
1868	1,653,384	£260	£330	£500	£850
1869	6,441,322	£260	£300	£400	£850
1870	2,189,960	£260	£300	£400	£850
1870	Inc. above / WW incuse	£270	£310	£450	£850
1871	8,767,250	£260	£300	£350	£600
1872	13,486,708	£260	£300	£350	£450
1872	Inc. above / No die number	£260	£300	£350	£500
1873	2,368,215	£260	£300	£350	£450
1874	520,713	£1k	£2k	£6k	

Melbourne mint coins, indicated here by an 'M' after the date and distinguished on the coin by a small 'M' under the wreath.

Date	Mintage	F	VF	EF	UNC
1872M	748,180 / 2 over 1	£300	£450	£850	£2000
1874M	1,373,298	£260	£300	£400	£800
1880M	3,053,454	£350	£650	£1500	£4000
1881M	2,324,800	£260	£300	£350	£1500
1882M	2,465,781	£260	£300	£350	£1500
1883M	427,450	£300	£500	£850	£1750
1884M	2,942,630	£260	£300	£400	£600
1885M	2,967,143	£260	£300	£350	£500
1886M	2,902,131	£800	£2500	£4500	£8000
1887M	1,916,424	£500	£1250	£3250	£6000

The image below shows the die number location on a shield back Victorian sovereign. The number '101' is shown here, but the die numbers do range from very low numbers to 3 digit figures.

They were used in order to log and gain some idea of the speed with which the dies became worn. Interestingly, when the young head Victorian sovereign dies were considered not good enough for use with sovereigns, the obverses were used to strike the obverses of the pre 1860 copper farthings.

Victoria Young head, shield
back 1871 Sovereign

Victoria - Young Head, shield reverse
Sydney mint coins, indicated here by an 'S' after the date and distinguished on the coin by a small 'S' under the wreath.

Date	Mintage/Notes	F	VF	EF	UNC
1871S	2,814,000	£260	£300	£350	£800
1873S	1,478,000	£260	£300	£400	£1000
1875S	2,122,000	£260	£300	£350	£800
1877S	1,590,000	£260	£300	£350	£600
1878S	1,259,000	£260	£300	£350	£500
1879S	1,366,000	£280	£380	£450	£800
1880S	1,459,000	£280	£350	£400	£600
1881S	1,459.000	£260	£300	£350	£600
1882S	1,209,000	£260	£300	£350	£1000
1883S	1,108,000	£260	£300	£350	£550
1884S	1,595,000	£260	£300	£350	£600
1885S	1,486,000	£260	£300	£350	£500
1886S	1,667,000	£260	£300	£350	£600
1887S	1,000,000	£260	£300	£400	£800

Victoria - Young Head, St George reverse
A change back to the St George reverse now, which is still used today. The shield back coins were produced simultaneously, but were mainly struck in the colonies. London mint coins are listed first.

Date	Mintage/Notes	F	VF	EF	UNC
1871	Inc. prev. page	BV	£250	£300	£500
1871	Longer horse tail, smaller B.P (approximately the same as above)				
1871	Proof				£5000
1872	Inc. prev. page	BV	£250	£300	£500
1873	Inc. prev. page	BV	£250	£300	£500
1874	Inc. prev. page	BV	£300	£400	£1500
1876	3,318,866	BV	£250	£300	£500
1878	1,091,275	BV	£250	£300	£500
1879	20,013	£400	£750	£2500	
1880	3,650,080	BV	£250	£300	£500
1880	Inc. above / Short horse tail	BV	£250	£300	£600
1880	Inc. above / no B.P	BV	£250	£350	£500
1880	Inc. above / 2nd 8 over 7	£300	£350	£400	£600
1880	Inc. above / 2nd 8 over 7, no B.P	£300	£350	£450	£550
1880	Inc. above / Longer horse tail	BV	£300	£400	£500
1884	1,769,635	BV	£300	£350	£500
1885	717,723	BV	£250	£350	£500

Victoria - Young Head, St George reverse

Melbourne mint coins, indicated here by an 'M' after the date and distinguished on the coin by a small 'M' under the bust of Queen Victoria.

Date	Mintage / Notes	F	VF	EF	UNC
1872M	748,180	£260	£300	£500	
1873M	751,199	BV	£300	£350	£800
1874M	1,373,298 / Varieties exist	BV	£300	£350	£1000
1875M	1,888,405 / Varieties exist	BV	£300	£350	£800
1876M	2,124,445	BV	£260	£300	£700
1877M	1,487,316 / Varieties exist	BV	£280	£300	£600
1878M	2,171,457	BV	£280	£300	£700
1879M	2,740,594 / Varieties exist	BV	£280	£300	£500
1880M	3,053,454 / Varieties exist	BV	£260	£290	£500
1881M	2,324,000	BV	£260	£290	£450
1881M	Inc. above / No B.P	BV	£300	£350	
1882M	2,465,781 / No B.P	BV	£260	£300	£800
1882M	Inc. above	BV	£260	£300	£900
1882M	Inc. above / Broader truncation	BV	£260	£350	
1883M	427,450	BV	£260	£300	£700
1883M	Inc. above / Broader truncation	BV	£260	£350	£600
1884M	2,942,630	BV	£260	£300	£600
1884M	Inc. above / No B.P	BV	£260	£300	£500
1884M	Inc. above / Broader truncation	BV	£260	£300	£500
1885M	2,967,143	BV	£300	£400	
1885M	Inc. above / Broader truncation	BV	£260	£300	£500
1886M	2,902,131	BV	£260	£290	£500
1887M	1,916,424	BV	£260	£290	£500

Victoria Young head, St. George reverse 1879 Melbourne mint Sovereign

The red spot in the image above shows the location of the mint letter when it is present under the bust of Queen Victoria.

Victoria - Young Head, St George reverse

Sydney mint coins, indicated here by an 'S' after the date and distinguished on the coin by a small 'S' under the bust of Queen Victoria.

Date	Mintage / Notes	F	VF	EF	UNC
1871S	2,814,000 / Short horse tail	£250	£350	£500	
1871S	Inc. above / Long horse tail	BV	£260	£300	
1872S	1,815,000	BV	£260	£300	
1873S	1,478,000	BV	£260	£300	£1000
1874S	1,899,000	BV	£260	£300	£1000
1875S	2,122,000	BV	£260	£300	£800
1876S	1,613,000	BV	£260	£300	£700
1879S	1,366,000	BV	£260	£300	£1200
1880S	1,459,000 / Long horse tail	BV	£260	£300	
1880S	Inc. above / W.W complete	BV	£260	£350	
1880S	Inc. above / No B.P	BV	£260	£300	
1881S	W.W wide spaced and short (values approximately as above)??				
1881S	1,360,000 / W.W complete	BV	£250	£280	
1882S	1,108,000 / No B.P	BV	£260	£300	£400
1882S	Inc. above / With B.P	BV	£260	£320	£600
1883S	1,108,000	BV	£260	£300	£1000
1884S	1,595,000	BV	£260	£300	£1000
1885S	1,486,000	BV	£260	£300	£700
1886S	1,667,000	BV	£260	£300	£500
1887S	1,000,000	BV	£260	£300	£450

Victoria Young head, St. George reverse 1887 Sydney mint Sovereign

Victoria - Jubilee Head, St George reverse
London mint coins first.

Date	Mintage / Notes	F	VF	EF	UNC
1887	1,111,280	BV	£250	£280	£350
1887	797 / Proof				£800
1888	2,277,424	BV	£250	£280	£350
1888	Inc. above / D:G: closer to crown	BV	£250	£300	£400
1889	7,257,455	BV	£250	£280	£340
1890	6,529,887	BV	£250	£280	£340
1891	Inc. below / Short horse tail	£300	£400	£800	
1891	6,329,476 / Longer horse tail	BV	£250	£280	£350
1892	7,104,720	BV	£250	£280	£350

Victoria Jubilee head 1893
Sydney mint Sovereign

Melbourne mint coins, indicated here by an 'M' after the date and distinguished
on the coin by a small 'M' under the horses rear right hoof.

1887M	940,000	BV	£260	£300	£400
1887M	Inc. above / Small spaced J E B	BV	£260	£300	£450
1888M	2,830,613 / Varieties exist	BV	£250	£300	£1000
1889M	2,732,590 / Varieties exist	BV	£250	£300	£400
1890M	2,473,537	BV	£250	£300	£800
1891M	2,749,592 / Varieties exist	BV	£250	£290	£600
1892M	3,488,750	BV	£250	£290	£400
1893M	1,649,352	BV	£250	£290	£400

Sydney mint coins, indicated here by an 'S' after the date and distinguished
on the coin by a small 'S' under the horses rear right hoof.

Date	Notes	F	VF	EF	UNC
1887S	1,002,000 / Varieties exist	BV	£260	£450	£1600
1887S	Proof	Rare			
1888S	2,187,000 / Varieties exist	BV	£260	£300	£500
1889S	3,262,000 / Varieties exist	BV	£260	£300	£400
1890S	2,808,000 / Varieties exist	BV	£260	£300	£400
1891S	2,596,000	BV	£260	£300	£400
1892S	2,837,000	BV	£260	£300	£400
1893S	1,346,000	BV	£260	£300	£400

Victoria - Widow Head, St George reverse
London mint coins first.

Date	Mintage / Notes	Fine	VF	EF	UNC
1893	6,898,260	BV	BV	£260	£350
1893	737 / Proof			£700	
1894	3,782,611	BV	BV	£260	£350
1895	2,285,317	BV	BV	£260	£350
1896	3,334,065	BV	BV	£260	£350
1898	4,361,347	BV	BV	£260	£350
1899	7,515,978	BV	BV	£260	£350
1900	10,846,741	BV	BV	£260	£350
1901	1,578,948	BV	BV	£260	£350

Victoria Veiled head
1900 Sovereign

Melbourne mint coins, indicated here by an 'M' after the date and distinguished on the coin by a small 'M' under the horses rear right hoof.

1893M	1,914,400	BV	BV	£260	£350
1894M	4,166,874	BV	BV	£260	£350
1895M	4,165,869	BV	BV	£260	£350
1896M	4,456,932	BV	BV	£260	£350
1897M	5,130,565	BV	BV	£260	£350
1898M	5,509,138	BV	BV	£260	£350
1899M	5,579,157	BV	BV	£260	£350
1900M	4,305,904	BV	BV	£260	£350
1901M	3,987,701	BV	BV	£260	£350

Sydney mint coins, indicated here by an 'S' after the date and distinguished on the coin by a small 'S' under the horses rear right hoof.

Date	Notes	Fine	VF	EF	UNC
1893S	1,346,000	BV	BV	£260	£350
1894S	3,067,000	BV	BV	£260	£350
1895S	2,758,000	BV	BV	£260	£350
1896S	2,544,000	BV	BV	£260	£350
1897S	2,532,000	BV	BV	£260	£350
1898S	2,548,000	BV	BV	£260	£350
1899S	3,259,000	BV	BV	£260	£350
1900S	3,586,000	BV	BV	£260	£350
1901S	3,012,000	BV	BV	£260	£350

Perth mint coins, indicated here by an 'P' after the date and distinguished on the coin by a small 'P' under the horses rear right hoof.

Date	Notes	Fine	VF	EF	UNC
1899P	690,992	£300	£350	£500	£1200
1900P	1,886,089	BV	BV	£260	£350
1901P	2,889,333	BV	BV	£260	£350

Edward VII
London mint coins first.

Date	Mintage / Notes	F	VF	EF	UNC
1902	15,123 / Matte Proof				£500
1902	4,737,796	BV	BV	£260	£320
1903	8,888,627	BV	BV	£250	£320
1904	10,041,369	BV	BV	£250	£320
1905	5,910,403	BV	BV	£250	£320
1906	10,466,981	BV	BV	£250	£320
1907	18,458,663	BV	BV	£250	£320
1908	11,729,006	BV	BV	£250	£320
1909	12,157,099	BV	BV	£250	£320
1910	22,379,624	BV	BV	£250	£320

Edward VII 1902 Sovereign

Ottawa (Canada) mint coins, indicated here by a 'C' after the date and
distinguished on the coin by a small 'C' under the horses rear right hoof.

1908C	636 / Proof			£5500	
1909C	16,273		BV	£400	£700
1910C	28,012		BV	£300	£400

Melbourne mint coins, indicated here by an 'M' after the date and
distinguished on the coin by a small 'M' under the horses rear right hoof.

1902M	4,467,157	BV	BV	£250	£320
1903M	3,521,780	BV	BV	£250	£320
1904M	3,743,897	BV	BV	£250	£320
1905M	3,633,838	BV	BV	£250	£320
1906M	3,657,853	BV	BV	£250	£320
1907M	3,332,691	BV	BV	£250	£320
1908M	3,080,148	BV	BV	£250	£320
1909M	3,029,538	BV	BV	£250	£320
1910M	3,054,547	BV	BV	£250	£320

Above: The enlarged reverse area of a 1902
Sovereign. The red spot shows the location (if
present) of the mint letter on St. George reverse sovereigns and half sovereigns from the
Jubilee Victoria type to the last colonial mint
sovereigns during the reign of George V.

Perth mint coins, indicated here by an 'P' after the date and
distinguished on the coin by a small 'P' under the horses rear right hoof.

1902P	4,289,122	BV	BV	£260	£320
1903P	4,674,783	BV	BV	£260	£320
1904P	4,506,756	BV	BV	£260	£320
1905P	4,876,193	BV	BV	£260	£320
1906P	4,829,817	BV	BV	£260	£320
1907P	4,972,289	BV	BV	£260	£320
1908P	4,875,617	BV	BV	£260	£320
1909P	4,524,241	BV	BV	£260	£320
1910P	4,690,625	BV	BV	£260	£320

Edward VII

Sydney mint coins, indicated here by an 'S' after the date and distinguished on the coin by a small 'S' under the horses rear right hoof.

Date	Mintage / Notes	F	VF	EF	UNC
1902S	2,813,000	BV	BV	£260	£330
1903S	2,806,000	BV	BV	£260	£330
1904S	2,896,000	BV	BV	£260	£330
1905S	2,778,000	BV	BV	£260	£330
1906S	2,792,000	BV	BV	£260	£330
1907S	2,539,000	BV	BV	£260	£330
1908S	2,017,000	BV	BV	£260	£330
1909S	2,057,000	BV	BV	£260	£330
1910S	2,135,000	BV	BV	£260	£330

George V - London mint coins first

1911	30,044,105	BV	BV	£250	£300
1911	3,764 / Proof			£500	
1912	30,317,921	BV	BV	£250	£300
1913	24,539,672	BV	BV	£250	£300
1914	11,501,117	BV	BV	£250	£300
1915	20,295,280	BV	BV	£250	£300
1916	1,554,120	BV	BV	£270	£350
1917	1,014,71		£3k	£7k	£10k
1925	4,406,431	BV	BV	£250	£300

George V 1914 Sovereign

Ottawa (Canada) mint coins, indicated here by a 'C' after the date and distinguished on the coin by a small 'C' under the horses rear right hoof.

1911C	256,946	BV	BV	£260	£340
1913C	3,715	£350	£700	£1400	
1914C	14,891	£250	£300	£450	£800
1916C	6,111	£2000	£6000	£10,000	
1917C	58,845	BV	£250	£280	£350
1918C	106,516	BV	£250	£280	£350
1919C	135,889	BV	£250	£280	£350

Bombay (India) mint coins, indicated here by an 'I' after the date and distinguished on the coin by a small 'I' under the horses rear right hoof.

1918I	1,294,372	BV	BV	£280	£350

Melbourne mint coins, indicated here by an 'M' after the date and distinguished on the coin by a small 'M' under the horses rear right hoof.

1911M	2,851,451	BV	BV	£250	£300
1912M	2,469,257	BV	BV	£250	£300
1913M	2,323,180	BV	BV	£250	£300
1914M	2,012,029	BV	BV	£250	£300
1915M	1,637,839	BV	BV	£250	£300

George V

Date	Mintage/Notes	F	VF	EF	UNC
1916M	1,272,634	BV	BV	£250	£300
1917M	934,469	BV	BV	£250	£300
1918M	4,809,493	BV	BV	£250	£300
1919M	514,257	BV	£270	£300	£450
1920M	530,266	£750	£1500	£3000	
1921M	240,121	Rare			
1922M	608,306	Rare			
1923M	511,129	BV	£270	£300	£400
1924M	278,140	BV	£260	£300	£350
1925M	3,311,662	BV	BV	£270	£300
1926M	211,107	BV	£260	£300	£400
1928M	413,208	Rare			
1929M	436,938	£600	£1000		
1930M	77,588	BV	£260	£300	£350
1931M	57,809	£260	£300	£350	£700

Perth mint coins, indicated here by a 'P' after the date and distinguished on the coin by a small 'P' under the horses rear right hoof.

1911P	4,373,165	BV	BV	£250	£300
1912P	4,278,144	BV	BV	£250	£300
1913P	4,635,287	BV	BV	£250	£300
1914P	4,815,996	BV	BV	£250	£300
1915P	4,373,596	BV	BV	£250	£300
1916P	4,096,721	BV	BV	£250	£300
1917P	4,110,286	BV	BV	£250	£300
1918P	3,812,884	BV	BV	£250	£320
1919P	2,995,216	BV	BV	£260	£320
1920P	2,421,196	BV	BV	£260	£320
1921P	2,314,360	BV	BV	£260	£320
1922P	2,298,884	BV	BV	£260	£320
1923P	2,124,154	BV	BV	£260	£320
1924P	1,464,416	£250	£280	£300	£350
1925P	1,837,901	£280	£300	£400	£500
1926P	1,313,578	£300	£400	£800	£1500
1927P	1,383,544	£280	£300	£350	£500
1928P	1,333,417	BV	BV	£280	£350
1929P	1,607,625	BV	BV	£280	£320
1930P	1,915,352	BV	BV	£280	£320
1931P	1,173,568	BV	BV	£250	£300

Sydney mint coins, indicated here by an 'S' after the date and distinguished on the coin by a small 'S' under the horses rear right hoof.

1911S	2,519,000	BV	BV	£250	£300
1912S	2,227,000	BV	BV	£250	£300
1913S	2,249,000	BV	BV	£250	£300
1914S	1,774,000	BV	BV	£250	£300
1915S	1,346,000	BV	BV	£250	£300
1916S	1,242,000	BV	BV	£260	£320

George V

Date	Mintage/Notes	F	VF	EF	UNC
1917S	1,666,000	BV	BV	£260	£330
1918S	3,716,000	BV	BV	£250	£300
1919S	1,835,000	BV	BV	£250	£300
1920S	360,000	Very rare			
1921S	839,000	£450	£800	£1200	£1800
1922S	578,000	£5000	£8000		
1923S	416,000	£3000	£5000		
1924S	394,000	£400	£650	£1000	
1925S	5,632,000	BV	BV	£250	£300
1926S	1,031,050	£5000	£7000		

Pretoria (South Africa) mint coins, indicated by an 'SA' after the date and distinguished by a small 'SA' under the horses rear right hoof.

1923SA	655	£2500	£3500		
1923SA	64 / Proof	Rare			
1924SA	3,184	£1500	£3500		
1925SA	6,086,000	BV	BV	£250	£300
1926SA	11,108,000	BV	BV	£250	£300
1927SA	16,379,999	BV	BV	£250	£300
1928SA	18,235,000	BV	BV	£250	£300
1929SA	12,024,000	BV	BV	£250	£300
1930SA	10,028,000	BV	BV	£250	£300
1931SA	8,512,000	BV	BV	£250	£300
1932SA	1,067,000	BV	BV	£250	£300

George V 1931 Pretoria mint (SA) Sovereign

Edward VIII
Extremely rare, not to be confused with modern fantasy patterns.

George VI
This issue was a plain edged proof only, struck in London. 5501 were struck, the odd '1' was for the King himself.

1937	5,501 / Plain edge Proof				£2000

Elizabeth II

1957	2,072,000	BV	BV	BV	£260
1958	8,700,000	BV	BV	BV	£260
1959	1,358,000	BV	BV	£250	£270
1962	3,000,000	BV	BV	BV	£260
1963	7,400,000	BV	BV	BV	£260
1964	3,000,000	BV	BV	BV	£260
1965	3,800,000	BV	BV	BV	£260
1966	7,050,000	BV	BV	BV	£260
1967	5,000,000	BV	BV	BV	£260
1968	4,203,000	BV	BV	BV	£260
(Decimal 1974 to 1982*)		BV	BV	BV	£260

*Coins were not struck every year.

George VI 1937 Proof and Elizabeth II first bust Sovereign obverses.

George III

Date	Mintage / Notes	F	VF	EF	UNC
1820	Pattern / Proof only	Rare			

George IV

1823	St. George reverse		£1500	£2000	£3000
1826	Proof (illustrated)				£7000
Other dates / proofs all very rare					

William IV

1831	225 / Proof				£14000

Victoria

1887	91,345 / Jubilee Head	£550	£650	£900	£1400
1887	797 / Jubilee Head Proof				£2500
1893	52,212 / Veiled Head	£600	£700	£1400	£2000
1893	773 / Veiled Head Proof				£4000

Edward VII

1902	45,807	£550	£650	£900	£1700
1902	8,066 / Proof				£1800

George V

Date	Notes	F	VF	EF	UNC
1911	2,812 / Proof				£2000

Edward VIII
Not issued.

George VI

Date	Notes	F	VF	EF	UNC
1937	5,501 / Proof				£2000

Elizabeth II
None until 1980.

George IV 1825 Proof Two Pound Coin

George VI 1937 Proof Two Pound Coin

George III

Date	Mintage/Notes	F	VF	EF	UNC
1820	Pattern/Proof only	Rare			

George IV

1826	Patten/Proof only	Rare			

William IV
Not issued.

Victoria

1839	Young head, proof only	Rare			
1887	53,844 / Jubilee Head	£1350	£1500	£2000	£3000
1887	797 / Jubilee Head Proof				£3000
1893	20,405 / Veiled Head	£1400	£1600	£2800	£4000
1893	773 / Veiled Head Proof				£12000

Edward VII

1902	34,911	£1350	£1500	£2000	£3000
1902	8,066 / Proof				£3000

Victoria 1893 Proof
Five Pound Coin

George V

1911	2,812 / Proof				£6000

Edward VIII
Not issued.

George VI

1937	5,501 / Proof				£5000

Elizabeth II
None until 1980.

Victoria 1887 Five Pound Coin

George V 1911 Proof
Five Pound Coin obverse

Coins not intended for circulation - Proof and Uncirculated Sets

Prices quoted are for sets in well preserved original cases of issue. There were individual proof coins struck for various years prior to 1826, but it was this date, under George IV, that officially produced proof sets were first made.

1826	Farthing - £5 coin	(11 coins)	Very Rare	£30,000+
1826	As above with 4 maundy coins.		Very Rare	£30,000+
1831	Farthing - £2 coin	(14 coins)	Very Rare	£30,000+
1839	Farthing - £5 coin	(15 coins)	Very Rare	£60,000+
1853	Half Farthing to 5s	(16 coins)	Very Rare	£50,000+
1887	3d to £5 coin. Jubilee head	(11 coins)	Very Rare	£12,500+
1887	3d to Crown	(7 coins)	Rare	£2,000+
1893	3d to £5 coin	(10 coins)	Very Rare	£12,500+
1893	3d to Crown	(6 coins)	Rare	£2,500+
1902	Maundy 1d - £5 coin	(13 coins)	Scarce (matte)	£5,000
1902	Maundy 1d - Sovereign	(11 coins)	Scarce	£1,500
1911	Maundy 1d - £5 coin	(12 coins)	Scarce	£12,000
1911	Maundy 1d - Sovereign	(11 coins)	Scarce	£3,000
1911	Maundy 1d - Half Crown	(8 coins)	Scarce	£950
1927	3d to Crown	(6 coins)	Scarce	£550
1937	Half Sovereign - £5	(4 coins)	Rare	£9,500
1937	Farthing - Crown & Maundy	(15 coins)	Common	£270
1950	Farthing - Half Crown	(9 coins)	Common	£100
1951	Farthing - Crown	(10 coins)	Common	£120
1953	Farthing - Crown	(10 coins)	Common	£90
1953	Farthing - Half Crown	(9 uncirculated coins)	Common	£20
1968/71	Blue folder 'last decimal set'		Very Common	£1
1970	Half Penny - Half Crown	(8 coins)	Very Common	£20

Silver pennies were historically the only coins that were given out at the Maundy ceremony*. From 1800 and possibly some years prior to this date, it is likely that the other small silver denominations (the fourpence, threepence and twopence) were also involved in the Maundy ceremony. Right up to the latter-most part of the reign of George III (and the 1816 re-coinage) the coins themselves were struck quite sporadically. George III never actually attended a Maundy ceremony, but as they certainly did occur, I would speculate that the money given out at the ceremony was made up of coins from circulation (with various dates) and not coins specially struck for the ceremony. No written records appear to exist to provide evidence of exactly what was handed out in the Maundy ceremonies of this reign. It is noted that the 1800 and later coins certainly seem to show up in excellent matching condition, which would imply that they were issued together (potentially every year from 1800 to 1816) and kept by some as mementos.

The George III dates in which the silver fourpence, threepence, twopence and penny coins were struck prior to the re-coinage of 1816 are as follows:

Fourpence: 1763, 1765, 1766, 1770, 1772, 1776, 1780, 1784, 1786, 1792, 1795 and 1800
Threepence: 1762, 1763, 1765, 1766, 1770, 1772, 1780, 1784, 1786, 1792, 1795 and 1800
Twopence: 1763, 1765, 1766, 1772, 1776, 1780, 1784, 1786, 1792, 1795 and 1800
Penny: 1763, 1766, 1770, 1772, 1776, 1779, 1780, 1781, 1784, 1786, 1792, 1795 and 1800

*According to P. Alan Rayner in "English Silver Coinage since 1649 (1992 edition)". To confuse things further, The Royal Mint website currently implies that the Charles II 1670 dated coins were the first Maundy money, which is odd because the earlier small silver coins hardly ever turn up today in anything other than well-used condition, which either means that they were never given out on a special occasion, or perhaps, also a perfectly logical conclusion; that they were simply seen as money and were spent by the poor souls who gratefully received them!

Complete Maundy Sets (1, 2, 3 and Fourpence coins)

Date	ESC	VF	EF	UNC/BU

GEORGE III .925 fine silver.
4 coins of 12mm, 14mm, 18mm and 19.5mm
Not all dates were struck. The dates listed below are the dates for which all of the one, two, three and fourpence coins were struck.

Date	ESC	VF	EF	UNC/BU
1763	2412	£200	£400	
1766	2414	£200	£400	
1772	2415	£200	£400	
1780	2416	£200	£400	
1784	2417	£200	£400	
1786	2418	£200	£400	
1792	2419	£400	£600	
1795	2420	£200	£400	
1800	2421	£100	£250	

Coins now smaller: 11mm, 13mm, 16mm and 18mm

Date	ESC	VF	EF	UNC/BU
1817	2422	£150	£250	
1818	2423	£150	£300	
1820	2424	£150	£350	

GEORGE IV .925 fine silver.
4 coins of 11mm, 13mm, 16mm and 18mm

Date	ESC	VF	EF	UNC/BU
1822	2425	£100	£180	£250/
1822	2426	Proof set		/£600
1823	2427	£100	£180	£250/
1824	2428	£100	£180	£300/
1825	2429	£90	£180	£250/
1826	2430	£90	£180	£250/
1827	2431	£90	£180	£300/
1828	2432	£90	£180	£250/
1828	2433	Proof set		/£750
1829	2434	£90	£180	£250/
1830	2435	£90	£180	£300/

WILLIAM IV .925 fine silver.
4 coins of 11mm, 13mm, 16mm and 18mm

Date	ESC	VF	EF	UNC/BU
1831	2436	£90	£150	£300/
1831	2437	Proof set		£350/£650
1831	2438	Proofs in gold		/£15,000
1832	2439	£90	£150	£300/
1833	2440	£90	£150	£300/
1834	2441	£90	£150	£300/
1835	2442	£90	£150	£300/
1836	2443	£100	£150	£300/
1837	2444	£100	£150	£300/

VICTORIA Young Head .925 fine silver.
4 coins of 11mm, 13mm, 16mm and 18mm

Date	ESC	VF	EF	UNC/BU
1838	2445		£200	£350/
1838	2446	Proof set		£300/
1838	2447	Proofs in gold		/£15,000

Date	ESC		EF	UNC/BU

VICTORIA (continued)

Date	ESC		EF	UNC/BU
1839	2448		£150	£300/
1839	2449	Proof set		£300/
1840	2450		£200	£300/
1841	2451		£200	£300/
1842	2452		£200	£300/
1843	2453		£200	£300/
1844	2454		£200	£300/
1845	2455		£200	£300/
1846	2456		£200	£300/
1847	2457		£200	£300/
1848	2458		£200	£300/
1849	2459		£200	£300/
1850	2460		£200	£300/
1851	2461		£200	£300/
1852	2462		£200	£300/
1853	2463		£200	£300/
1853	2464	Proof set		£400/
1854	2465		£150	£300/
1855	2466		£150	£300/
1856	2467		£150	£300/
1857	2468		£150	£300/
1858	2469		£150	£300/
1859	2470		£150	£300/
1860	2471		£150	£300/
1861	2472		£150	£300/
1862	2473		£150	£300/
1863	2474		£150	£300/
1864	2475		£150	£300/
1865	2476		£150	£300/
1866	2477		£150	£300/
1867	2478		£150	£300/
1867	2479	Proof set		£400/
1868	2480		£150	£300/
1869	2481		£150	£300/
1870	2482		£140	£300/
1871	2483		£140	£300/
1871	2484	Proof set		£500/
1872	2485		£140	£250/
1873	2486		£140	£250/
1874	2487		£140	£250/
1875	2488		£140	£250/
1876	2489		£140	£250/
1877	2490		£140	£250/
1878	2491		£140	£250/
1878	2492	Proofs	£300	£400/

Date	ESC	EF	UNC/BU	Date	ESC	EF	UNC/BU
VICTORIA (continued)				GEORGE V (continued)			
Young Head .925 fine silver.				1912	2529	£80	£100/£140
4 coins of 11mm, 13mm, 16mm and 18mm				1913	2530	£80	£100/£140
1879	2493	£100	£200/	1914	2531	£80	£100/£140
1879	ND Proofs		£1,000	1915	2532	£80	£100/£140
1880	2494	£100	£200/	1916	2533	£80	£100/£140
1881	2495	£100	£200/	1917	2534	£80	£100/£140
1881	2495A Proofs		£300+/	1918	2535	£80	£100/£140
1882	2496	£100	£200/	1919	2536	£80	£100/£140
1883	2497	£100	£200/	1920	2537	£80	£100/£140
1884	2498	£100	£200/	1921	2538	£80	£100/£140
1885	2499	£100	£200/	1922	2539	£85	£100/£140
1886	2500	£100	£200/	1923	2540	£80	£100/£140
1887	2501	£110	£200/	1924	2541	£80	£100/£140
Jubilee Head				1925	2542	£80	£100/£140
1888	2502	£100	£150/	1926	2543	£80	£100/£140
1888	2503 Proofs	?	?	1927	2544	£80	£100/£140
1889	2504	£100	£150/	1928	2545	£80	£100/£140
1890	2505	£100	£150/	1929	2546	£80	£100/£140
1891	2506	£100	£150/	1930	2547	£80	£100/£140
1892	2507	£100	£150/	1931	2548	£80	£100/£140
Old/Widow Head				1932	2549	£80	£100/£140
1893	2508	£80	£100/	1933	2550	£80	£100/£140
1894	2509	£80	£100/	1934	2551	£80	£100/£140
1895	2510	£80	£100/	1935	2552	£80	£100/£140
1896	2511	£80	£100/	1936	2553	£80	£100/£140
1897	2512	£80	£100/	GEORGE VI types as above, .500 silver.			
1898	2513	£90	£125/	1937	2554		£90/£140
1899	2514	£90	£125/	1938	2555		£90/£140
1900	2515	£90	£120/	1939	2556		£90/£140
1901	2516	£80	£100/	1940	2557		£90/£140
				1941	2558		£90/£140
EDWARD VII types the same.				1942	2559		£90/£140
1902	2517	£80	£100/	1943	2560		£90/£140
1902	2518 Matt Proofs		/£120	1944	2561		£90/£140
1903	2519	£80	£100/	1945	2562		£90/£140
1904	2520	£80	£120/	1946	2563		£90/£140
1905	2521	£80	£120/£160	Silver reverted to .925 Fine.			
1906	2522	£80	£120/	1947	2564		£90/£140
1907	2523	£80	£120/	1948	2565		£90/£140
1908	2524	£80	£120/	1949	2566		£90/£140
1909	2525	£90	£150/	1950	2567		£90/£140
1910	2526	£90	£150/	1951	2568		£90/£140
				1952	2569		£90/£140
GEORGE V types as Edward VII, .500 silver from 1921.							
1911	2527	£80	£100/				
1911	2528 Proof set		/£100				

Original boxes add value.
Add £10 - £15 for a set housed in
contemporary dated case.

Date	ESC		UNC/BU

ELIZABETH II .925 fine silver.
4 coins of 11mm, 13mm, 16mm & 18mm

Date	ESC		UNC/BU
1953	1,025		£400/£600
1953	In gold	(1985)	£5,750
1954			£100/£150
1955			£100/£150
1956			£100/£150
1957			£100/£150
1958			£100/£150
1959			£100/£150
1960			£100/£150
1961			£100/£150
1962			£100/£150
1963			£100/£150
1964			£100/£150
1965			£100/£150
1966			£100/£150
1967			£100/£150
1968			£100/£150
1969			£100/£150
1970			£100/£150

Left: George III 1800 maundy set. The last set before the current sizes were adopted in 1817. Below: 1882 Victoria maundy set. The reverse types have remained very similar ever since.

Victoria 1898 Maundy Groat

Maundy obverses usually use the same bust as the circulation coinage. With the exception that the laureate George IV bust was used for all George IV maundy money and the first Elizabeth II bust has been, and is still being used for all Elizabeth II maundy money.

Maundy Singles

The earlier silver fourpence, threepence, twopence and to a lesser-degree the pennies from the reign of George III do appear to have circulated as currency, so are probably not strictly 'maundy money'. In this edition they are included here with the maundy coins, but will be moved to the main section for the next edition.

It is generally preferred to collect complete maundy sets rather than try to obtain each date individually, mainly because individual coins can be difficult to track down of certain dates, and it can work out more expensive. Also, complete sets tend to all have the same toning, and they therefore match better. Individual coins do often appear for sale with prices varying greatly. Below is a list of approximate prices for coins in Uncirculated condition:

George III 1763-1795* coins:	EF
Fourpence	£40-£80
Threepence	£30-£60
Twopence	£30-£60
Penny	£30-£60

*Not all years were struck. 1765 two, three and fourpence coins are considerably rarer and more expensive.

1800 set	UNC
Fourpence	£50 - £100
Threepence	£50 - £100
Twopence	£40 - £80
Penny	£30 - £70

1817 - 1820 type	
Fourpence	£30 - £40
Threepence	£30 - £40
Twopence	£20 - £30
Penny	£20 - £30

George IV	
Fourpence	£20 - £40
Threepence 1822	£40 - £50
Threepence (others)	£20 - £30
Twopence	£15 - £30
Penny	£15 - £40

William IV	
Fourpence	£20 - £40
Threepence	£30 - £50
Twopence	£20 - £40
Penny	£15 - £40

Victoria Young Head (1838 - 1887)	UNC
Fourpence	£20 - £30
Threepence	£35 - £40
Twopence	£15 - £20
Penny	£10 - £20

Victoria Jubilee Head (1888 - 1892)	
Fourpence	£15 - £25
Threepence	£20 - £30
Twopence	£10 - £20
Penny	£10 - £20

Old Head (1893 - 1901)	
Fourpence	£15 - £25
Threepence	£20 - £30
Twopence	£10 - £20
Penny	£10 - £20

Edward VII & George V	
Fourpence	Around £15
Threepence	£15 - £20
Twopence	£10 - £15
Penny	£10 - £15

George VI and Elizabeth II up to 1970 except 1953 coins, which are expensive	
Fourpence	Around £25
Threepence	Around £25
Twopence	Around £25
Penny	Around £30

A Glossary Numismatic terms and Abbreviations

Many of the abbreviations used in this book are standard coin collectors' jargon, there are however, a few that may not be so obvious. This glossary should clear things up:

Alignment:	The relationship between the obverse and reverse of the coin. Either the reverse is up side down compared to the obverse when rotated with fingers at the top and bottom of the coin, or the reverse is up the same way when the coin is rotated with fingers at the top and bottom of the coin. The latter is the most common alignment for British coins dated 1860-date and may be referred to in this book as up/up. In the same way the upside down alignment may sometimes be referred to as up/down.
Berries:	Usually refers to the number of berries in the wreath around the monarch's head.
BV:	Bullion Value. i.e. no collectors premium over the value of the metal.
H:	An 'H' after the date in the first column indicates the coin was struck at the Heaton Mint in Birmingham. The 'H' mintmark will appear on the coin either next to, or under its date.
Incuse:	Struck inwards. Lettering or a design element on a coin that is the opposite to raised. For example, the edge lettering on the modern £1 coin.
KN:	A 'KN' after the date in the first column indicates the coin was struck at the Kings Norton Mint in Birmingham. The 'KN' will appear on the coin next to the date.
Modified Effigy:	(George V only) In the absence of a direct comparison, the modified effigy (or modified head) can be distinguished by the initials which appear on the truncation of the neck. Before modification, the initials B.M. are placed near the centre of truncation. After modification they appear, without stops, well to the right thus: BM (not B.M.) The initials are those of the designer of the coin: Bertram Mackennal.
Mule:	A Mule is when a coin gets made with the wrong combination of obverse and reverse.
Obverse:	(or Obv) The side of the coin with the head of the Monarch on.
Pattern:	A proposed coin type that was not used for circulation.
Piedfort:	A coin that is struck on a thicker blank than is usual. Relatively recently the Royal mint starting coining Silver Piedfort coins.
Pointing/Points:	To distinguish a different die used to strike a particular coin, often 'pointings' are used. They normally refer to a letter or design element on the coin, and to whether it points directly at, or between two border teeth or another element of the coin.
Proof:	A special striking of a coin using specially prepared and polished dies and blanks.
Reverse:	(or Rev) The opposite side of the coin to the obverse, or the 'tails' side.
Teeth/Beads:	The small teeth or circles surrounding the inner rim of many British coins. Beads are circular, teeth are elongated.
Truncation:	(or trunc) The base of the monarch's neck, often containing the designers initials.

The following books were used as reference during the writing of this book, and are recommended for further reading:

Previous editions of "Collectors' Coins Great Britain". (out of print)

"The British Bronze Penny", by Michael Gouby.
(Available from the author: www.michaelcoins.co.uk)
"English Copper, Tin and Bronze coins in the British Museum 1558-1958",
by C Wilson Peck. (out of print)
"Handbook of the Coins of Great Britain & Ireland (1899)",
by H A Grueber (available new, as a facsimile of the original)
"Kenyon's Gold Coins of England (1884)",
by Robert Lloyd Kenyon. (out of print)
"The Bronze Coinage of Great Britain", by Michael J Freeman. (Available new from Rotographic)
"English Silver Coinage since 1649", by Maurice Bull. (Available new)
"British Silver Coins Since 1816", by Peter J Davies. (Available new)
"Standard Catalog of World Coins", by C L Krause and C Mishler. (Available new, published in the USA)
"A Guide Book of English Coins", by K E Bressett. (Out of print but often available second hand on eBay, published in the USA)
"The Sovereign", by Daniel Fearon / Brian Reeds. (Available new)
"The Identification of British 20th Century Bronze Coin Varieties", by D J Groom. (Available new)
"The Identification of British 20th Century Silver Coin Varieties", by D J Groom. (Available new)
Also recommended is: "The Early British Bronze Bun Penny 1860 - 1865 and their varieties", by John Jerrams.

The Cover Coin

The cover coin this year is an 1860 bronze penny reverse with a beaded border. In Michael Freeman's incredibly detailed 'The Bronze Coinage of Great Britain' it is coin no. 5 - a copper proof with a bronzed finish, struck on an extra heavy flan. The fantastic drawing in the background is a line drawing of an 1847 'Gothic' crown and is one of 36 drawings of coins found in 'The Coin Colouring Book' which was first published by Rotographic in October 2017.

Copyright Notice

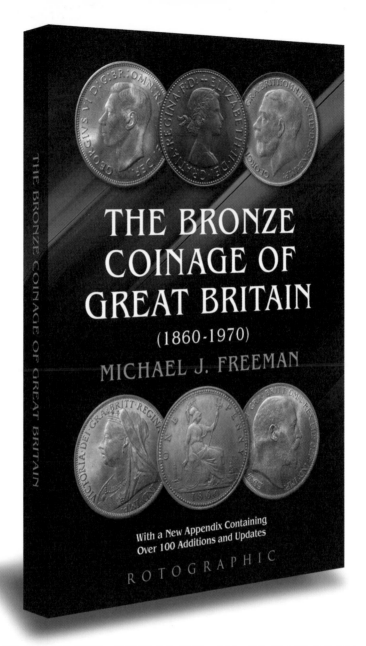

THE BRONZE COINAGE OF GREAT BRITAIN
by Michael J. Freeman
Published June 2016, containing new infomation.

RRP: £14.00. ISBN: 978 094864 84 8